STAR WARS®

SAVE the GALAXY!

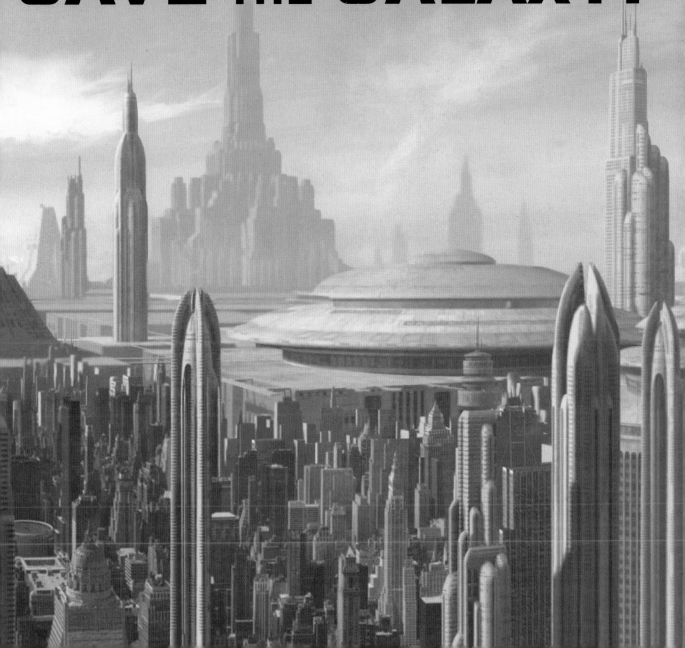

STAR WARS®

SAVE the GALAXY!

WRITTEN BY JASON FRY AND DANIEL WALLACE

CONTENTS

"DO YOU REALLY THINK IT WILL COME TO WAR?"

When Emperor Palpatine builds the most powerful battle station the galaxy has ever seen, it seems as though the Sith have triumphed. But in every battle there are heroes: Heroes who will fight even if they are outnumbered. Heroes who will attack a weapon as dangerous as the Death Star to restore freedom to the galaxy.

22 BBY: Battle of Geonosis

19 BBY: Birth of Luke and Leia

41 BBY: Birth of Anakin

32 BBY: Battle of Naboo

19 BBY: Jedi Purge

50 BBY **40 BBY** **30 BBY** **20 BBY**

REPUBLIC ERA

THE CLONE WARS

■ Accurate data is crucial in a battle situation. Throughout the book, look for pieces of mission data in special boxes like these.

TIMES OF WAR

Throughout the galaxy, great conflicts have been decided on the battlefield. No one wants war, but sometimes fighting is necessary to free people who are suffering, or to defeat an evil tyrant. The Jedi Knights, the Republic's clone army, and the Rebel Alliance all fight hard to defeat powerful enemies through warfare.

So who are these skilled soldiers? What secrets do they know about combat on unfamiliar planets and in the emptiness of outer space? And how can they make you ready to face your own foes? Take a seat, Recruit, and prepare for your mission briefing!

NOTE ON DATES: Dates are fixed around the Battle of Yavin in year 0. All events prior to this are measured in terms of years Before the Battle of Yavin (BBY). Events after it are measured in terms of years After the Battle of Yavin (ABY).

0 Battle of Yavin

3 ABY: Battle of Hoth

2 BBY: Rebel Alliance is founded

4 ABY: Battle of Endor

10 BBY   0   10 ABY   20 ABY

DROID DATA

■ Droids are full of surprises. Throughout the book, look out for extra details about droids in special boxes like this.

Most droids don't take sides: they simply obey their master. But some droids are built to wage war, and their brains are programmed to be loyal to their cause. During the Clone Wars, the Separatists deploy an enormous Droid Army, made up of thousands of battle droids who will stop at nothing to defeat their enemies.

32 BBY: C-3PO
MEETS R2-D2

22 BBY: BATTLE
OF GEONOSIS

19 BBY: JEDI PURGE

19 BBY: DEACTIVATION
OF TRADE FEDERATION
BATTLE DROIDS

41 BBY: BIRTH OF
ANAKIN

32 BBY: BATTLE
OF NABOO

50 BBY

40 BBY

30 BBY

20 BBY

REPUBLIC ERA

THE CLONE WARS

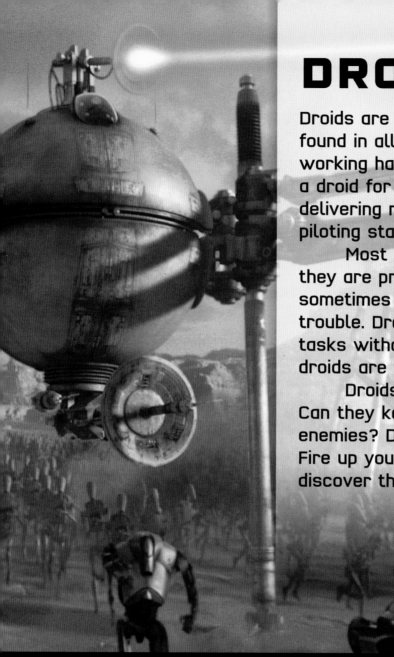

DROIDS

Droids are everywhere! They can be found in all corners of the galaxy, working hard at their tasks. There is a droid for every job—whether it's delivering messages, spying, cooking, piloting starships, or fighting wars.

Most droids can do only what they are programmed to, although sometimes faulty wiring can cause trouble. Droids usually go about their tasks without complaining, but some droids are fussier than others.

Droids can surprise you. Can they keep secrets? Trick their enemies? Do they ever make friends? Fire up your data receivers and discover the secret life of droids!

0: BATTLE OF YAVIN

3 ABY: BATTLE OF HOTH

4 ABY: BATTLE OF ENDOR

REPUBLIC

The Republic is a democracy. It aims to govern life in the galaxy freely and fairly. Every planet has a vote and the chance to voice its opinion. But some members of the Republic have other ideas...

JEDI ORDER

The Jedi are the peacekeepers of the galaxy. They work together with the rulers of the Republic to ensure that laws are being obeyed. After the Clone Wars, the surviving Jedi join the Rebel Alliance.

SENATE

The Senate is the government of the Republic. Some Senators join the Separatists, and the Senate later becomes part of the Empire.

Senators who oppose the Empire join the Rebels.

CLONE ARMY

The Republic controls a huge army of clone troopers. When the Empire later takes control, the clone troopers become stormtroopers.

CHANCELLOR

Chancellor Palpatine is the leader of the Republic. He directs the Senate and tries to keep the galaxy peaceful. But he is hiding a dark secret...

REBELS

LUKE SKYWALKER

Luke is the last remaining Jedi. He joins

LEIA ORGANA

Princess Leia is a daring Senator. She does not agree with

HAN SOLO

Han Solo is a smuggler. At first he helps the Rebels for

When the Republic becomes the Empire, those who decide to

Battles rage across the galaxy. Governments rise and fall. The Clone Wars saw the Republic ravaged by the Separatists—and turned into the Empire. Use this page to learn about the people and organizations that have shaped the history of the galaxy, for good or for evil.

SEPARATISTS

There are some people who believe the Republic is corrupt. They want to take control of the galaxy. They call themselves the Confederacy of Independent Systems, or Separatists.

DARTH SIDIOUS
Chancellor Palpatine is really the Sith Lord Darth Sidious in disguise. Sidious manipulates both sides of the Clone Wars as part of his quest to turn the galaxy into an Empire.

TRADE FEDERATION
The Trade Federation is an organization that controls most of the trade in the galaxy. It is run by greedy Neimoidians who care only about making a profit.

APPRENTICE
Count Dooku is Darth Sidious's Sith apprentice. He leads the Separatists under Sidious's command. Dooku is killed when Sidious seeks a new, more powerful apprentice.

DROID ARMY
Built by the Trade Federation, the droid army fights for the Separatists. When the clone army joins the Empire, the droids are decommissioned.

EMPIRE

EMPEROR
Darth Sidious installs himself as the Emperor—the chief ruler of the galaxy. He is a ruthless, deadly tyrant and is feared by all.

DARTH VADER
Jedi Anakin Skywalker turns to the dark side and becomes Darth Sidious's new apprentice, Darth Vader. Vader directs the Imperial Army.

IMPERIAL ARMY
The Republic clone army becomes the Imperial Army. Clone troopers are now stormtroopers and enforce Imperial rule across the galaxy.

At the end of the Clone Wars, what's left of the Republic becomes the Empire—a tyrannical dictatorship ruled by a Sith: Emperor Palpatine.

DROID ARMY STATS

LEADER: COUNT DOOKU
ALLEGIANCE: SEPARATISTS
HEADQUARTERS: GEONOSIS
WEAPONS: BLASTER RIFLE, BLASTER PISTOL, THERMAL DETONATOR
VEHICLES: STAP, MTT, AAT, DROID TRI-FIGHTER
VALUES: OBEDIENCE TO PROGRAMMING

CHAIN OF COMMAND

DARTH SIDIOUS (IN SECRET)
COUNT DOOKU
GENERAL GRIEVOUS
COMMANDER BATTLE DROIDS
BATTLE DROIDS

Super battle droids have thick armor and blasters built into their arms. They aren't as common as regular battle droids but they are much harder to destroy.

RADIATION SENSORS TO SEE IN THE DARK

SUPER BATTLE DROID

TWIN RAPID-FIRE BLASTER CANNONS

DROIDEKAS

DROIDEKAS LOOK LIKE THEIR INSECTOID ALIEN BUILDERS

DEADLY ROLLERS

Droidekas, or destroyer droids, have their own shield generators. They can also transform into a wheel and roll toward a target. They are so fast and powerful, they sometimes make Jedi Knights retreat!

FEDERATION FUNDING
Big corporations like the Trade Federation supply the money to build the droid army, although Count Dooku is the army's official leader. Of course, the Sith Lord Darth Sidious is secretly behind it all!

BATTLE DROID

DROID IS DIRECTED FROM CENTRAL COMMAND SIGNAL

E-5 BLASTER

FRAGILE CONSTRUCTION

Droid ARMY

The Separatists use droid soldiers to fight their battles. Droids never get tired, always obey orders, and can be easily replaced when damaged. Battle droids, super battle droids, and droidekas may not be very smart, but they can be deadly!

EXPENDABLE
B1 battle droids are the Separatists' foot soldiers. They are easy to defeat but can be dangerous if many attack at once. Droid commanders have yellow markings and are slightly more independently minded.

BOSS NASS

EXPENSIVE
CEREMONIAL
ROBES OF OFFICE

LEADER OF THE PACK

This proud Gungan is the head of the Gungan High Council and ruler of the capital city Otoh Gunga. As commander-in-chief of all soldiers and warfare, he has gathered Gungan military units from many different tribes to join forces in this all-out assault against the invaders.

BIG DISTRACTION

Holding energy shields, Gungan soldiers form a strong battle line against marching droids. Their mission is to distract the Trade Federation from events occurring in Theed while Queen Amidala regains control

COUNCIL WISDOM

The Gungan High Council advises Boss Nass on matters important to his undersea capital, Otoh Gunga. The Jedi try to convince the Gungan people to fight, but at first they don't listen.

GUNGAN ARMY STATS

LEADER: BOSS NASS

ALLEGIANCE: REPUBLIC

HEADQUARTERS: OTOH GUNGA, NABOO

WEAPONS: ATLATL, CESTA, BOOMA, CATAPULT

VEHICLES: WAR WAGON, KAADU, MOUNTED FAMBAA

VALUES: NATIVE PRIDE, BRAVERY

MILITIAGUNGS USE A STICK CALLED AN ATLATL TO THROW BLUE PLASMA BALLS

PLASMA BALLS (BOOMAS) ARE MINED FROM NABOO'S CORE

MILITIAGUNG

CHAIN OF COMMAND

BOSS NASS

BOMBAD GENERAL

GUNGAN OFFICERS

CAVALRY/MILITIAGUNGS

AMPHIBIOUS GUNGANS DON'T LIKE FIGHTING ON LAND

Gungan
ARMY

The Naboo-dwelling Gungans have an impressive army, but they don't plan on fighting. However, when Queen Amidala informs them that the Trade Federation's battle droids are a threat to their entire planet, the Gungans grab their weapons and prepare for action!

GUNGAN WEAPONS
Gungan warriors are also known as militiagungs. They use atlatls or long sticks (called cestas) to throw plasma balls (boomas) into battle. Some militiagungs ride into battle on the backs of animals

NABOO

PLANET: Naboo
LOCATION: Mid Rim
TERRAIN: Grassy plains, swamps, deep seas
INHABITANTS: Humans (the Naboo), Gungans
ALLEGIANCE: Republic

The Trade Federation, controlled by the Sith Lord Darth Sidious, has invaded the planet Naboo to provoke war. Although they are greatly outnumbered, Queen Amidala, her Royal Security Forces, two Jedi Knights, and the Gungan Jar Jar Binks unite to fight back. Working together, these allies hope to put an end to the invasion—a goal that requires six dangerous missions.

1. GRASSY PLAINS

OBJECTIVE:
Gungans to create a diversion for the droid army.

OUTCOME:
Battle begins, droids are successfully distracted.
MISSION COMPLETE.

2. THEED PALACE

OBJECTIVE:
Queen Amidala and her soldiers to sneak into the royal palace.

OUTCOME:
Team avoids battle droids and enters through window.
MISSION COMPLETE.

3. SPACE BATTLE

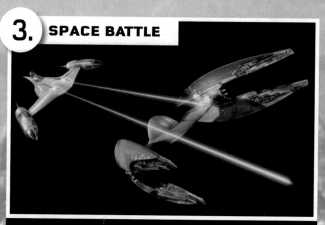

OBJECTIVE:
Naboo starfighter pilots to attack the Droid Control Ship.

OUTCOME:
Pilots engage hostile vulture droids, but suffer losses.
MISSION INCOMPLETE.

> # "This is a battle I do not think we can win."
>
> **Captain Panaka,**
> **Naboo Royal Security Forces**

BATTLE STATS

TRADE FEDERATION:

- SITH
- BATTLE DROIDS
- DROIDEKAS
- DROID CONTROL SHIP
- VULTURE DROIDS

PEOPLE OF NABOO:

- JEDI
- NABOO SOLDIERS
- GUNGAN ARMY
- NABOO N-1 STARFIGHTERS
- WEAPONS: LIGHTSABERS, BLASTERS, ENERGY BALLS

4. SITH DUEL

OBJECTIVE:
Jedi to eliminate the Sith Darth Maul.

OUTCOME:
Obi-Wan kills Maul, but Qui-Gon also dies. MISSION COMPLETE.

5. THEED THRONE ROOM

OBJECTIVE:
Queen Amidala to capture the Trade Federation viceroy, Nute Gunray.

OUTCOME:
Using a decoy, the Queen confuses the viceroy and makes him surrender. MISSION COMPLETE.

6. DROID CONTROL SHIP

OBJECTIVE:
Naboo pilots to destroy the Droid Control Ship.

OUTCOME:
Anakin blows up the ship from the inside, shutting down the droid army. MISSION COMPLETE.

CONSEQUENCES

The Battle of Naboo is a success for Naboo. Once again, the planet is under the rule of its Queen, and the Trade Federation has lost power. However, the battle sparks a crisis in the government of the Republic, and Palpatine becomes the new Chancellor. No one knows it yet, but this is his first step in leading the galaxy into an even bigger war.

Pieces of wrecked droids litter the battlefield. Jar Jar gets one stuck to his foot and just wants to shake it loose. As the enemy closes in from every side, Jar Jar's attempts to shake the robot off make it fire its weapon. First one battle droid goes down, then another, then another!

WHEN THE TRADE FEDERATION invades Naboo, the planet's inhabitants, the Gungans, are ready to fight. But Jar Jar Binks isn't so sure. This awkward Gungan misfit doesn't want to be a hero, let alone a General. When the battle begins, Jar Jar fumbles, bumbles, and panics—but somehow his antics destroy a large part of the enemy army!

WHAT GOOD IS CLUMSINESS ON THE BATTLEFIELD?

Hoping to escape from the blaster fire and explosions, Jar Jar tries to hitch a ride on a war wagon. His clumsiness causes the wagon to spill open, unleashing destructive plasma energy balls. These weapons conveniently collide with the attacking droids.

THE SEPARATISTS

The Separatist military has one major difference from other armies—it is made up almost entirely of droids. Many war machines that normally require pilots or drivers are replaced with big, specially designed robots. Droids attack in huge waves and can be replaced easily. The Separatists hope this is enough to bring them victory!

ARMORED ASSAULT TANK (AAT)
- **SIZE** 9.75 m (32 ft) LONG
- **SPEED** 55 km/hr (34 mph)
- **CAPACITY** 4 CREW, 6 BATTLE DROIDS ON EXTERIOR
- **WEAPONS** 1 HEAVY LASER CANNON, 2 SECONDARY LASER CANNONS, 6 PROJECTILE LAUNCHERS

CRAB DROID
- **SIZE** 1.49 m (4.9 ft) TALL
- **SPEED** 35 km/hr (22 mph)
- **CAPACITY** NONE
- **WEAPONS** TWIN BLASTER CANNONS, WATER JET SPRAYER

DROIDEKA (DESTROYER DROID)
- **SIZE** 1.83 m (6 ft) TALL
- **SPEED** 75 km/hr (47 mph)
- **CAPACITY** NONE
- **WEAPONS** 2 TWIN BLASTER CANNONS

MULTI-TROOP TRANSPORT (MTT)
- **SIZE** 31 m (101.7 ft) LONG
- **SPEED** 35 km/hr (22 mph)
- **CAPACITY** 4 CREW, 112 BATTLE DROIDS
- **WEAPONS** 4 TWIN BLASTER CANNONS

CORPORATE ALLIANCE TANK DROID
- **SIZE** 10 m (32.8 ft) LONG
- **SPEED** 50 km/hr (31 mph)
- **CAPACITY** NONE
- **WEAPONS** 2 LASER CANNONS, 2 ION CANNONS, MISSILE LAUNCHER

HAILFIRE DROID
- **SIZE** 6.8 m (22.3 ft) TALL
- **SPEED** 45 km/hr (28 mph)
- **CAPACITY** NONE
- **WEAPONS** 1 LASER CANNON, 2 MISSILE LAUNCHER ARRAYS

OCTUPTARRA DROID
- **SIZE** 14.6 m (48 ft) TALL
- **SPEED** 25 km/hr (16 mph)
- **CAPACITY** NONE
- **WEAPONS** 3 LASER CANNONS

SENSORS CAN SEE IN COMPLETE DARKNESS

DESTROYS ENEMY VEHICLES WITH ONE SHOT

LAND

DWARF SPIDER DROID
- **SIZE** 1.98 m (6.5 ft) TALL
- **SPEED** 30 km/hr (19 mph)
- **CAPACITY** NONE
- **WEAPONS** 1 HEAVY BLASTER CANNON

GOOD AT CROSSING ROUGH GROUND

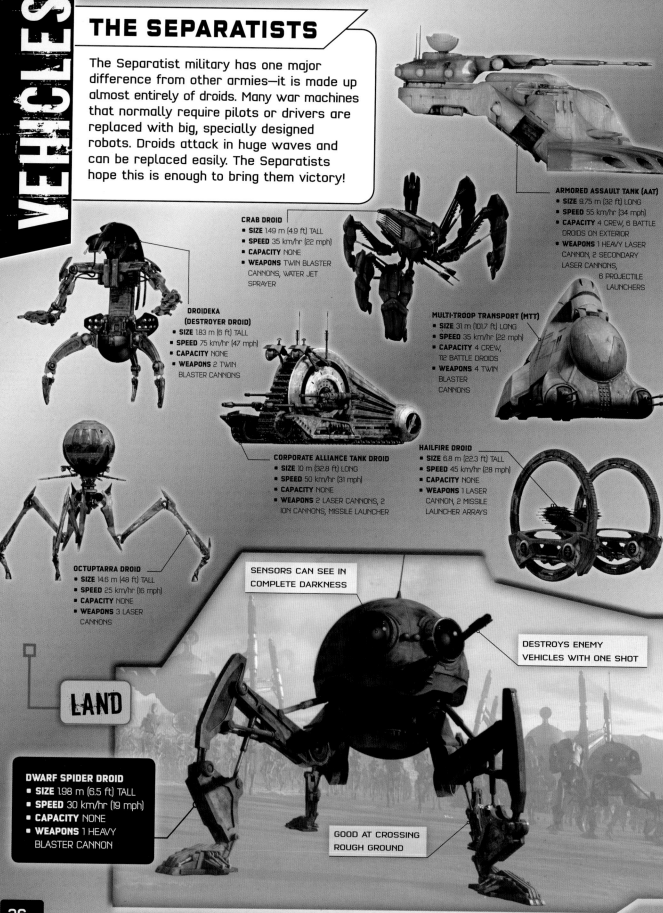

SENDS DROID
CONTROL SIGNAL

BATTLESHIP CORE CAN
SEPARATE FROM RING

DROID CONTROL SHIP
- **SIZE** 3,170 m (10,400 ft)
  DIAMETER
- **MAX ACCELERATION** 300 G.
- **CAPACITY** 350 CREW,
  100,000 PASSENGERS
- **WEAPONS** 185 QUAD LASERS,
  520 LASER CANNONS,
  51 TURBOLASERS

SPACE

CARRIES 1,500 DROID
STARFIGHTERS

BUZZ DROID
- **SIZE** 0.25 m (0.8 ft) DIAMETER
- **SPEED** 20 km/hr (12 mph)
- **CAPACITY** NONE
- **WEAPONS** PLASMA TORCHES,
  DRILLS, CIRCULAR SAWS,
  PINCERS, HOOKS

DROID TRI-FIGHTER
- **SIZE** 5.4 m (17.7 ft) LONG
- **MAX ACCELERATION** 3,600 G
- **CAPACITY** NONE
- **WEAPONS** 1 LASER CANNON,
  3 LIGHT LASER CANNONS,
  MISSILE LAUNCHER

VULTURE DROID STARFIGHTER
- **SIZE** 3.5 m (11.5 ft) LONG
- **MAX ACCELERATION** 3,900 G
- **CAPACITY** NONE
- **WEAPONS** 4 BLASTER
  CANNONS, 2 MISSILE
  LAUNCHERS

SPACE/AIR

**SINGLE TROOPER AERIAL
PLATFORM (STAP)**
- **SIZE** 2 m (6.6 ft) TALL
- **SPEED** 400 km/hr
  (249 mph)
- **CAPACITY** 1 PILOT
- **WEAPONS** 1 TWIN
  BLASTER CANNON

AIR

BUILT-IN
DROID BRAIN

BODY SUPPORTS MISSILE RACKS

LASER
CANNON

CARRIES MISSILES, BOMBS,
OR PROTON TORPEDOES

DROID GUNSHIP
- **SIZE** 12 m (40 ft) LONG
- **SPEED** 820 km/hr (510 mph)
- **CAPACITY** NONE
- **WEAPONS** 2 TWIN LASER CANNONS,
  1 MEDIUM LASER CANNON, 2 LIGHT LASER
  CANNONS, 2 MISSILE LAUNCHERS

HOW CAN YOU STOP A DROID ARMY?

...300,
...warriors are
...fighting the invading
...oldiers one at a
...t they are
...bered. The droid
...as one weakness:
...robot is controlled
...gle huge ship floating
...Naboo. A strike at the
...of the droids' power
...top the army, but
...no easy task.

Anakin Skywalker is strong in the Force and a great Podracer pilot, but he has never flown a starfighter. However, Anakin isn't afraid. He has faced and overcome dangers on the Podracing track, and his confidence helps him join the other Naboo pilots in their daring fight.

The droid armies on the surface can't operate without a signal from their control ship. Thanks to Anakin's amazing shot, every droid soldier freezes in its tracks. The Gungan warriors are triumphant!

When Anakin fires two proton torpedoes at attacking droids, it accidentally starts a chain reaction that destroys the huge Droid Control Ship— he barely escapes the gigantic explosion!

JEDI GENERAL PLO KOON

THICK, PROTECTIVE SKIN

CHAIN OF COMMAND

JEDI GRAND MASTER

JEDI COUNCIL

JEDI GENERALS

JEDI COMMANDERS

CLONE TROOPERS

Jedi GENERALS

HIGH FLYER
During the Clone Wars, General Plo Koon develops a reputation as a fierce starship pilot. His loyalty to the clone troopers under his command is legendary.

Members of the Jedi Order study the secrets of the Force and use their wisdom to protect the galaxy. They would prefer to be peacekeepers rather than warriors, but when galactic peace is threatened, the Jedi are forced to take a more aggressive approach.

WAR FOR PEACE

In times of crisis, the Jedi Order must fight for justice and democracy. Jedi Knights and Masters become Generals, while Padawans become Commanders. During the Clone Wars, General Obi-Wan Kenobi oversees a legion of clone troopers. His second-in-command is Clone Commander Cody, with whom he develops a close bond.

A Jedi must be able to adapt to his military role at a moment's notice. For most members of the Jedi Council, the Battle of Geonosis is the very first time they assume the role of General.

MASTER OF LIGHTSABER COMBAT FORM III (SORESU)

JEDI GENERAL OBI-WAN KENOBI

STRATEGY MEETINGS
The Jedi Council directs the Republic's military effort. Using holoprojectors, any location can serve as a briefing room, including the Kashyyyk command center.

JEDI STATS
LEADER: YODA

ALLEGIANCE: REPUBLIC

HEADQUARTERS: JEDI TEMPLE, CORUSCANT

WEAPONS: LIGHTSABERS

VEHICLES: DELTA-7 STARFIGHTERS, ETA-2 INTERCEPTORS

VALUES: JUSTICE, HONOR, DEMOCRACY, INTEGRITY

BATTLE ANALYSIS:
GEONOSIS

PLANET: Geonosis

LOCATION: Remote sector of Outer Rim

TERRAIN: Dusty, rocky, with spire hives

INHABITANTS: Insectoid Geonosians

ALLEGIANCE: Separatists

New information from Obi-Wan Kenobi has revealed that the Separatists—led by Count Dooku—have built an enormous droid army. The Republic has access to a secret army of clones. When Obi-Wan is captured by Count Dooku, the Galactic Senate and the Jedi Council agree to take decisive action. The Republic sends envoys and troops to Geonosis, with orders to undertake six crucial missions.

1. DROID FACTORY

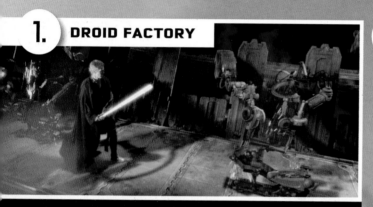

OBJECTIVE:
Anakin Skywalker and Padmé Amidala to rescue Obi-Wan Kenobi.

OUTCOME:
Anakin Skywalker and Padmé Amidala captured. MISSION FAILED.

2. EXECUTION ARENA

OBJECTIVE:
Anakin, Padmé, and Obi-Wan to escape execution.

OUTCOME:
Captives survive and destroy vicious beasts. MISSION COMPLETE.

3. JEDI STRIKE FORCE

OBJECTIVE:
Jedi team to rescue captives from droids.

OUTCOME:
Many Jedi killed, Jedi survivors surrounded by droid army. MISSION INCOMPLETE.

"Begun, the CLONE WARS have." Yoda

BATTLE STATS

SEPARATISTS:

- BATTLE DROIDS
- SUPER BATTLE DROIDS
- SPIDER DROIDS
- DROIDEKAS
- WEAPONS: BLASTER RIFLES

REPUBLIC:
- JEDI
- CLONE TROOPERS
- AT-TE WALKERS
- LAAT/I GUNSHIPS
- WEAPONS: BLASTER RIFLES, LIGHTSABERS

4. ARRIVAL OF CLONE ARMY

OBJECTIVE:
Clone army to rescue survivors.

OUTCOME:
Survivors airlifted out of arena. MISSION COMPLETE.

5. DESERT BATTLE

OBJECTIVE:
Jedi to lead clone troopers and vehicles against droid army.

OUTCOME:
Despite many fatalities during a full-scale battle, clone army is victorious. MISSION COMPLETE.

CONSEQUENCES

The Battle of Geonosis concludes with heavy losses on both sides, including hundreds of Jedi. After a fierce duel, Count Dooku escapes with plans for a Death Star. Palpatine, as Supreme Chancellor, has taken control of the Republic as the Clone Wars begin.

6. DUEL WITH DOOKU

OBJECTIVE:
Obi-Wan, Anakin, and Yoda to prevent Count Dooku's escape from Geonosis.

OUTCOME:
Anakin loses his arm, Count Dooku escapes. MISSION FAILED.

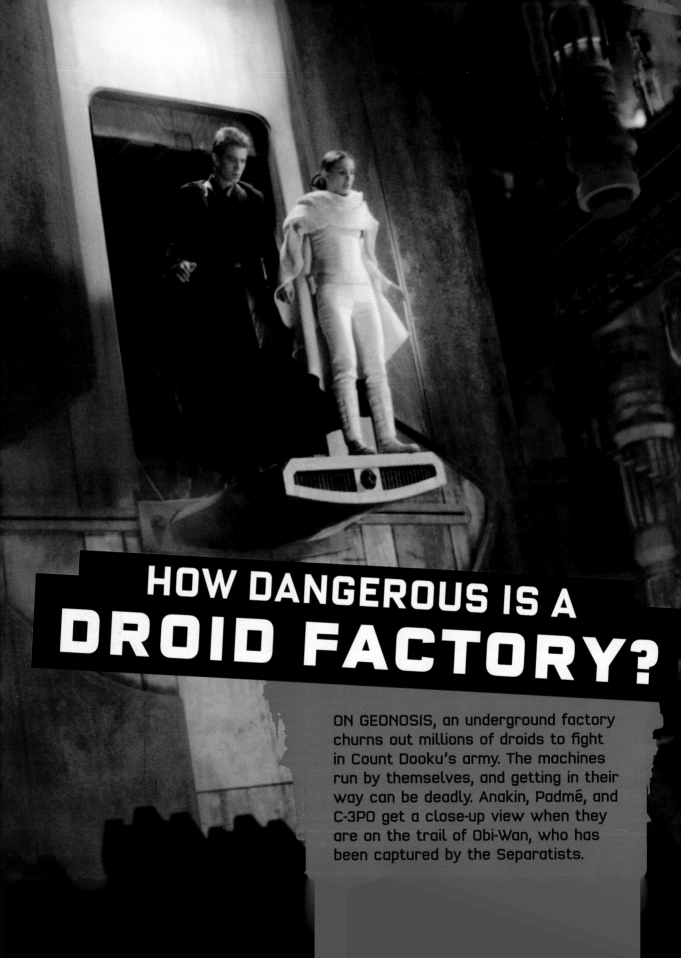

HOW DANGEROUS IS A DROID FACTORY?

ON GEONOSIS, an underground factory churns out millions of droids to fight in Count Dooku's army. The machines run by themselves, and getting in their way can be deadly. Anakin, Padmé, and C-3PO get a close-up view when they are on the trail of Obi-Wan, who has been captured by the Separatists.

To the factory machine, there's no difference between battle droids and protocol droids. A blade knocks off C-3PO's head and welds it onto a new battle droid body. Luckily, C-3PO can survive losing his head, though the fretful droid finds it all very confusing.

Anakin fights Geonosian warriors on the moving belts until a machine clamps his right arm under a piece of metal! He eventually gets loose, but his lightsaber is ruined.

MISSION DATA

■ Battle droids are made by other droids, as humans are too easily injured. C-3PO is amazed at the huge operation: "Machines making machines!" he marvels.

Padmé is nearly covered in red-hot metal, but R2-D2 switches off the pouring machine just in time. Padmé is free, but she quickly discovers the most dangerous things in the droid factory are the Geonosians who guard it!

BUILT-IN
COMLINK

DC-15
BLASTER
RIFLE

Clone
ARMY

The Republic doesn't have a military unit of its own, so finding a ready-made army of clone fighters on Kamino seems too good to be true! As the Jedi Generals lead their new soldiers into battle against the Separatists, they don't realize that their troopers are secretly loyal to Darth Sidious.

The clone army is equipped with starfighters, tanks, speeders, and warships. On Coruscant, thousands of clones march into troop carriers on their way to fight the Separatists.

PHASE I ARMOR

ARMOR HAS
20 SEPARATE
PIECES

RESTRICTIVE ARMOR
The early clone troopers wore Phase I armor with its distinctive helmet fin and pure white color. Made of plastoid, the armor provided protection against explosions and shrapnel, but it wasn't very easy to move around in. It was soon replaced with Phase II armor.

CHAIN OF COMMAND
CHANCELLOR PALPATINE

JEDI GENERALS

CLONE COMMANDERS

CLONE CAPTAINS

CLONE LIEUTENANTS

CLONE SERGEANTS

CLONE TROOPERS

BORN TO FIGHT

Each clone is grown from the DNA of the bounty hunter Jango Fett. Clones are designed to age twice as fast as normal humans and are trained for a life of combat.

CLONE ARMY STATS

LEADER: CHANCELLOR PALPATINE
ALLEGIANCE: REPUBLIC
HEADQUARTERS: CORUSCANT
WEAPONS: BLASTER RIFLE, BLASTER CARBINE
VEHICLES: AT-TE WALKER, REPUBLIC GUNSHIP, SPHA-T WALKER, BARC SPEEDER REPUBLIC ASSAULT GUNBOAT, CLONE TURBO TANK, AT-RT WALKER, SWAMP SPEEDER, REPUBLIC ARTILLERY GUN
VALUES: TEAM UNITY, OBEDIENCE

PHASE II ARMOR

DC-15A BLASTER FIRES 500 SHOTS FROM A SINGLE GAS CARTRIDGE

POUCHES CONTAIN MEDICAL KIT AND EXTRA AMMUNITION

ARMOR HAS SPECIAL ANTI-BLASTER COATING

ARMOR UPDATES

The Phase II armor is designed with improvements learned from battle experience. It is more comfortable, stands up to blaster fire, and comes in camouflage colors when required.

37

IDENTIFICATION

You can't win a war without adapting to changing circumstances. At the start of the Clone Wars, every trooper wore identical armor. But as the fighting spread to hundreds of planets, clone armor became customized to get the job done better. Color markings now denote unit affiliation, while extra equipment or design adjustments adapt the armor to suit the needs of individual missions.

trooper armor is plain white and blaster resistant. However, it is not always suitable for working in extreme environments or handling specialized equipment.

CLONE COMMANDERS

COMMANDER NEYO
Leader of the 91st Reconnaissance Corps, Neyo is an expert BARC speeder pilot. His helmet has been adjusted so it is extra streamlined.

COMMANDER BLY
Bly serves with the Star Corps. The viewfinder on his helmet provides better visibility in the jungles of Felucia.

COMMANDER CODY
The troopers of the 212th Attack Battalion report to Cody, who stays in control with built-in radio antennas.

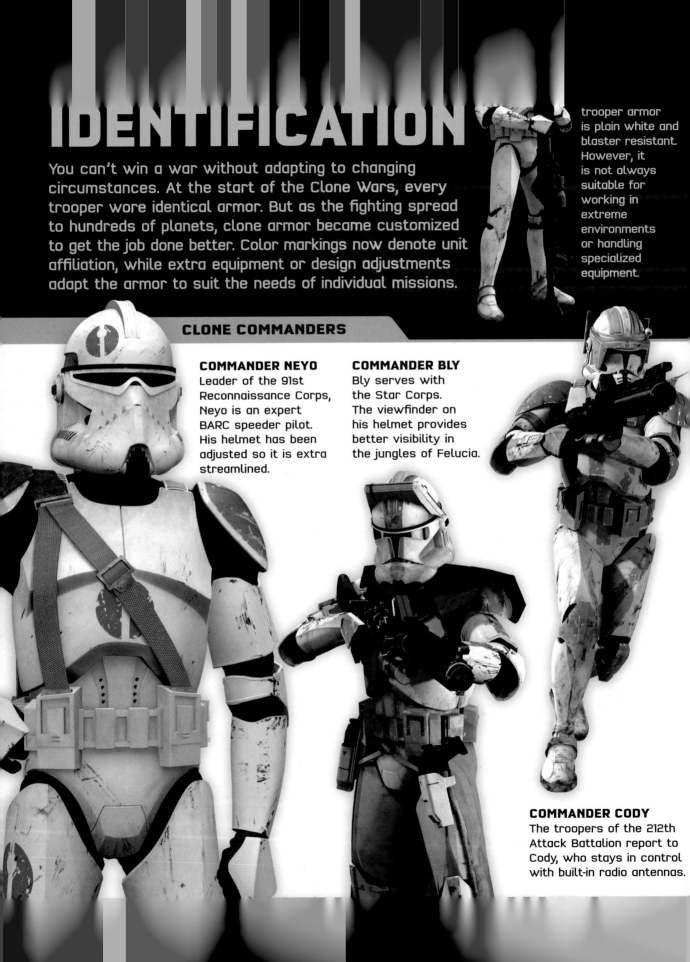

SHOCK TROOPER
Shock Troopers are members of the Coruscant Guard. They act as bodyguards for Chancellor Palpatine and other important officials, and are easily identifiable by the red markings on their armor.

CLONE PILOT
Pilots can fly everything from ARC-170s to V-wings. Their armor contains a life-support pack.

AT-RT DRIVER
AT-RT drivers wear camouflage armor and have a lifeform scanner attached to their gun strap.

COMMANDER GREE
Gree is an expert in alien cultures. When working with the Wookiees on the jungle planet Kashyyyk, he wears green camouflage armor.

GALACTIC MARINE
Members of the 21st Nova Corps, Marines are trained to fight in many environments, and their Synthmesh helmet screens keep out sand, dust, and grit.

ENVIRONMENT SPECIALISTS

COMMANDER BACARA
Bacara is one of the leaders of the Galactic Marines. He wears the maroon colors of the Marines, and a protective kama around his waist to indicate rank.

SWAMP TROOPER
With lightweight, camouflaged armor, swamp troopers can operate on soggy planets where heavy equipment would just sink into mud.

VEHICLES

THE REPUBLIC

During the Clone Wars, enormous Republic assault ships and cruisers transport thousands of Jedi and clone forces to battlefields across the galaxy. Walkers, tanks, starfighters, and gunships are commanded by clones on land, in the sky, and in space! The Jedi have powerful vessels, too; their ships are fast and nimble.

ALL TERRAIN TACTICAL ENFORCER (AT-TE)
- **SIZE** 22m (72 ft) LONG
- **SPEED** 60 km/hr (37 mph)
- **CAPACITY** 45 TROOPERS
- **WEAPONS** 6 ANTI-PERSONNEL CANNONS, 1 MASS-DRIVER CANNON

ALL TERRAIN OPEN TRANSPORT (AT-OT)
- **SIZE** 14.3 m (47 ft) LONG
- **SPEED** 55 km/hr (34 mph)
- **CAPACITY** 35 TROOPERS
- **WEAPONS** 4 LASER CANNONS

SWAMP SPEEDER
- **SIZE** 5 m (16.4 ft) LONG
- **SPEED** 100 km/hr (62 mph)
- **CAPACITY** 1 PILOT, 1 GUNNER
- **WEAPONS** 2 BLASTER CANNONS

CLONE TURBO TANK
- **SIZE** 49.4 m (162.1 ft) LONG
- **SPEED** 160 km/hr (99 mph)
- **CAPACITY** 300 TROOPERS
- **WEAPONS** 1 HEAVY LASER CANNON, 1 REPEATING LASER CANNON, 2 ANTI-PERSONNEL LASER CANNONS, 2 BLASTER CANNONS, 2 GRENADE LAUNCHERS

ALL TERRAIN ATTACK POD (AT-AP)
- **SIZE** 11 m (36.1 ft) TALL
- **SPEED** 60 km/hr (37 mph)
- **CAPACITY** 1 PILOT, 2 GUNNERS
- **WEAPONS** 1 HEAVY BLASTER CANNON, 1 MEDIUM BLASTER CANNON, 1 PROJECTILE LAUNCHER

ALL TERRAIN RECON TRANSPORT (AT-RT)
- **SIZE** 3.2 m (10.5 ft) TALL
- **SPEED** 75 km/hr (47 mph)
- **CAPACITY** 1 PILOT
- **WEAPONS** 1 LASER CANNON

LAND

TURBOLASER DESTROYS ESCAPING STARSHIPS

WEAPON CAN BE REPLACED WITH ION CANNON OR MISSILE LAUNCHER

THICK ARMOR

CLONE COMMANDERS WATCH BATTLEFIELD AND GIVE ORDERS

12 LEGS PROVIDE STABILITY

SELF-PROPELLED HEAVY ARTILLERY-TURBOLASER (SPHA-T)
- **SIZE** 140.2 m (460 ft) LONG
- **SPEED** 35 km/hr (22 mph)
- **CAPACITY** 15 CREW, 10 GUNNERS
- **WEAPONS** 1 TURBOLASER, 12 ANTI-PERSONNEL LASERS

40

COCKPIT

GUNSHIPS ARE NOT HEAVILY ARMED AND TRY TO AVOID ENEMY FIRE

REPUBLIC GUNSHIP
- **SIZE** 17.4 m (57.1 ft) LONG
- **SPEED** 620 (km/hr) (385 mph)
- **CAPACITY** 4 CREW, 30 TROOPERS
- **WEAPONS** 4 LASER TURRETS, 3 ANTI-PERSONNEL LASER TURRETS, 2 MISSILE LAUNCHERS, 8 AIR-TO-AIR MISSILES

CLONE GUNNERS TRACK THEIR TARGETS

FORWARD LASER

BIKER ADVANCED RECON COMMANDO (BARC) SPEEDER
- **SIZE** 4.57 m (15 ft) LONG
- **SPEED** 520 km/hr (323 mph)
- **CAPACITY** 1 PILOT
- **WEAPONS** 2 LIGHT BLASTER CANNONS

AIR

ARC-170 STARFIGHTER
- **SIZE** 14.5 m (47.6 ft) LONG
- **MAX ACCELERATION** 2.600 G
- **CAPACITY** 2 PILOTS, 1 GUNNER
- **WEAPONS** 4 LASER CANNONS, 1 TORPEDO LAUNCHER

REPUBLIC ASSAULT SHIP
- **SIZE** 752 m (2,467 ft) LONG
- **MAX ACCELERATION** 3,500 G
- **CAPACITY** 700 CREW, 16,000 TROOPERS
- **WEAPONS** 12 QUAD TURBOLASERS, 24 LASER CANNONS, 4 TORPEDO LAUNCHERS

JEDI INTERCEPTOR
- **SIZE** 5.47 m (18 ft) LONG
- **MAX ACCELERATION** 5,200 G
- **CAPACITY** 1 PILOT
- **WEAPONS** 2 LASER CANNONS, 2 ION CANNONS

REPUBLIC ATTACK CRUISER
- **SIZE** 1,137 m (3,730 ft) LONG
- **MAX ACCELERATION** 3,000 G
- **CAPACITY** 7,400 CREW, 2,000 TROOPERS
- **WEAPONS** 8 HEAVY TURBOLASER TURRETS, 2 DUAL TURBOLASER CANNONS, 52 LASER CANNONS, 6 TRACTOR BEAM PROJECTORS, 4 TORPEDO LAUNCHERS

SPACE

ASTROMECH DROID REPAIRS DAMAGE

COMPACT SIZE

JEDI STARFIGHTER
- **SIZE** 8 m (26.2 ft)
- **SPEED** 5,000 G
- **CAPACITY** 1 PILOT
- **WEAPONS** 2 TWIN LASER CANNONS

ION CANNON KNOCKS OUT ENEMY SHIP'S ELECTRONICS

S-FOIL WING PANEL

REPUBLIC CRUISER
- **SIZE** 115 m (377.3 ft) LONG
- **MAX ACCELERATION** 2,040 G
- **CAPACITY** 8 CREW, 16 PASSENGERS
- **WEAPONS** NONE

WHAT HAPPENS WHEN DROIDS FIGHT CLONES?

AT THE BATTLE OF GEONOSIS, Count Dooku's droid army is huge, and the Republic's clone troopers are outnumbered and outgunned. However, they are smarter than their robot foes. It is the clone troopers' first fight—and they are ready!

■ The clone troopers have been training for nearly ten years. Their cloning center on Kamino has areas where the troopers practice military missions and strategy.

Clone troopers are living beings, who can outthink battle droids. Officers direct the battle from a clone command station, which means they take control of the battlefield. Some of the Trade Federation's ships try to escape but the clone troopers quickly shoot them down.

Droids follow each other without question. If one droid is destroyed, a dozen more can take its place. Clone troopers, however, can think for themselves and react to changing situations—a skill that saves lives and wins battles.

43

DARTH VADER

BETRAYED

Darth Tyranus used to be a Jedi called Count Dooku. He thinks he's more important than everyone else, but he doesn't realize that Darth Sidious is using him in order to gain a more powerful apprentice—until Darth Sidious orders Anakin to kill him.

Darth Sidious tempts Anakin Skywalker into joining the Sith so he can become more powerful. Consumed by the dark side, Anakin takes the name Darth Vader and attacks his former friends.

DARTH VADER WILL REPLACE ANAKIN'S LIGHTSABER WITH A RED-BLADED ONE

Sith LORDS

The Sith have been the enemies of the Jedi for thousands of years. They follow the dark side of the Force and thrive on anger, greed, and fear. They crave power above everything else and use war as a tool to weaken their enemies.

SITH STATS

LEADER: DARTH SIDIOUS
ALLEGIANCE: THEMSELVES
HEADQUARTERS: CORUSCANT
WEAPONS: RED-BLADED LIGHTSABERS, FORCE LIGHTNING, FORCE CHOKING
VEHICLES: SITH SPEEDER, SITH INTERCEPTOR
VALUES: POWER AT ANY COST

DEEP WRINKLES CAUSED BY FORCE LIGHTNING

DARTH SIDIOUS

ELABORATE REGAL ROBES SIGNIFY POWER AND IMPORTANCE

CALLOUS LEADER

This evil Sith Lord works in secret, tricking others into doing what he wants. Posing as a man called Palpatine, he becomes Chancellor of the Senate so he can control the Republic. He starts the Clone Wars and uses the conflict to make himself Emperor, ruler of the galaxy.

MISSION DATA

■ Sith are so hungry for power that they even kill each other. Because of this, the Rule of Two states that there can only be two Sith at a time: one Master and one apprentice.

MASTER:
DARTH SIDIOUS

APPRENTICES:
FIRST: DARTH MAUL
SECOND: DARTH TYRANUS
THIRD: DARTH VADER

WHAT HAPPENS
WHEN THE TWO SIDES
OF THE FORCE MEET?

WHEN A JEDI FACES a Sith, the light and dark sides of the Force crash together like ocean waves. The Sith love destruction and their dark side powers may seem more powerful. However, the Jedi have faith that the light side will win in the end.

MISSION DATA

■ The Sith tap into dark emotions to use Force lightning, but a skilled Jedi can deflect the attacks safely. Yoda fights without ever giving in to anger or frustration.

Anyone can use a lightsaber, but only those attuned to the Force can get the most out of the weapon. Yoda's and Darth Sidious's sword skills are equally matched so they must draw on other Force powers to triumph in battle.

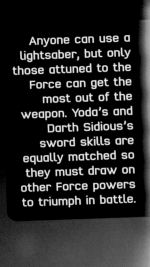

Yoda may be small but he is strong in the Force. He uses the power of the Force jump to add height and reach to his lightsaber moves—and to surprise and confuse his enemy in combat.

Dark side followers often take the easy way out. The Sith are willing to attack innocents to gain an edge. Yoda uses telekinesis to save his fellow Jedi from being crushed, while Dooku quietly escapes.

47

BLASTER PISTOLS

Blaster pistols can be fired with only one hand and are easy to carry on a belt (or hide under a cloak). Most blaster pistols have stun settings and high-powered settings, so you can choose whether to knock out your enemies —or completely destroy them.

Aurra Sing's Blaster Pistol

Clone Trooper Blaster Pistol

Naboo Blaster Pistol

Bail Organa's Blaster Pistol

Blaster Pistol

General Grievous's Blaster Pistol

Stormtrooper Blaster Pistol

Captain Panaka's Blaster Pistol

Blaster Pistol

Naboo Blaster Pistol

Battle Droid Blaster Pistol

Captain Typho's Blaster Pistol

Blaster Pistol

Naboo Blaster Pistol

Naboo Blaster Pistol

Blaster Pistol

Tatooine Blaster Pistol

Blaster Pistol

Coruscant Blaster Pistol

Blaster Pistol

Naboo Blaster Pistol

Tatooine Blaster Pistol

TOOLS OF WAR

A good soldier never goes into battle unarmed. Wookiees are super strong and Jedi can control the Force, but even these warriors know the value of a well-placed weapon. Blaster pistols and rifles can strike from long distances, while lightsabers and electrostaffs are perfect for close-range combat.

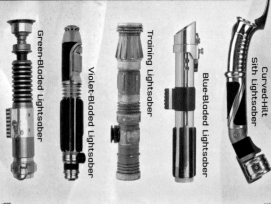

Green-Bladed Lightsaber

Violet-Bladed Lightsaber

Training Lightsaber

Blue-Bladed Lightsaber

Curved-Hilt Sith Lightsaber

Double-Bladed Sith Lightsaber

LIGHTSABERS ▲

For a thousand generations, Jedi Knights have carried these energy swords. Most Jedi lightsabers have green or blue blades, while Sith lightsabers are usually red. Some lightsabers even have two blades.

Mustafarian Blaster Rifle

Clone Trooper Blaster Rifle

Neimoidian Blaster Rifle

Utapaun Blaster Rifle

Coruscant Senate Guard Blaster Rifle

Geonosian Sonic Blaster Rifle

Boba Fett's Blaster Rifle

▶ BLASTER RIFLES

These heavy blaster weapons must be carried with two hands, but they can fire further and more accurately than blaster pistols. Clone troopers and stormtroopers are never seen without blaster rifles on the battlefield.

Clone Trooper Blaster Rifle

Imperial Stormtrooper Blaster Rifle

Tatooine Thunderblaster Rifle

Flash Speeder Gun

Electrostaff

Thermal Detonator

Naboo Laser Light

MISCELLANEOUS WEAPONS

Warriors need to adapt to their situation. Use a laser light to signal friends, and a saberdart to strike distant foes. Electrostaffs take out one enemy at a time, while thermal detonators can clear out an entire room.

Saberdart

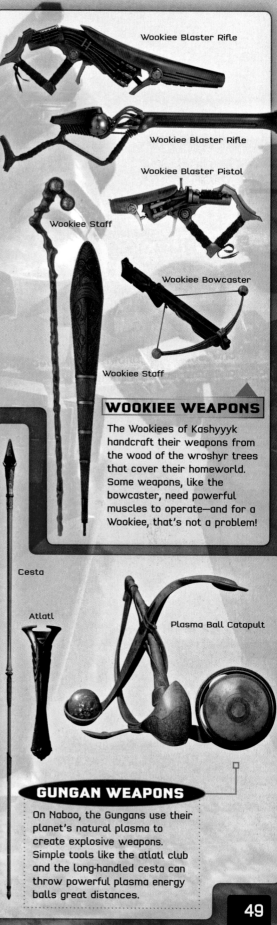

Wookiee Blaster Rifle

Wookiee Blaster Rifle

Wookiee Blaster Pistol

Wookiee Staff

Wookiee Bowcaster

Wookiee Staff

WOOKIEE WEAPONS

The Wookiees of Kashyyyk handcraft their weapons from the wood of the wroshyr trees that cover their homeworld. Some weapons, like the bowcaster, need powerful muscles to operate—and for a Wookiee, that's not a problem!

Cesta

Atlatl

Plasma Ball Catapult

GUNGAN WEAPONS

On Naboo, the Gungans use their planet's natural plasma to create explosive weapons. Simple tools like the atlatl club and the long-handled cesta can throw powerful plasma energy balls great distances.

49

CORUSCANT

PLANET: Coruscant
LOCATION: Core worlds
TERRAIN: One single gigantic city, including the seat of the Republic's government
INHABITANTS: Humans plus many different alien species
ALLEGIANCE: Republic

With the Clone Wars in full swing, Separatist warships surround the Republic capital of Coruscant. Their plot is not conquest—it's kidnapping! Chancellor Palpatine is a prisoner aboard General Grievous's command ship, *Invisible Hand.* It's up to Obi-Wan Kenobi and Anakin Skywalker to rescue the Republic ruler. If they can eliminate some of the Separatist commanders along the way, they might help the Republic make progress in the Clone Wars.

1. INVISIBLE HAND

OBJECTIVE:
Anakin and Obi-Wan to fight their way to Grievous's flagship.

OUTCOME:
The Jedi defeat droids and land successfully on *Invisible Hand.* MISSION COMPLETE.

BATTLE STATS

SEPARATISTS:
- BUZZ DROIDS
- BATTLE DROIDS
- VULTURE DROIDS
- MAGNAGUARDS
- WEAPONS: ELECTROSTAFFS, LIGHTSABERS, BLASTERS

REPUBLIC:
- ARC-170 STARFIGHTERS
- ETA-2 INTERCEPTORS
- REPUBLIC ATTACK CRUISERS
- CLONE TROOPERS
- WEAPONS: LIGHTSABERS, BLASTERS

2. PALPATINE

OBJECTIVE:
Jedi to find the Chancellor aboard the huge ship.

OUTCOME:
Palpatine is located with help from R2-D2. MISSION COMPLETE.

"Time to abandon SHIP!"

General Grievous

3. SITH DUEL

OBJECTIVE:
Anakin and Obi-Wan to capture Count Dooku.

OUTCOME:
Count Dooku defeated and killed by Anakin. MISSION INCOMPLETE.

4. ESCAPE

OBJECTIVE:
Rescue party to get off the flagship before it's destroyed by the Republic fleet.

OUTCOME:
Rescue party is captured. Republic attack damages the ship. MISSION FAILED.

5. GENERAL GRIEVOUS

OBJECTIVE:
Jedi to eliminate General Grievous, leader of the Separatist army.

OUTCOME:
Grievous's MagnaGuards are destroyed, but the general escapes. MISSION FAILED.

6. ROCKY LANDING

OBJECTIVE:
Anakin to land the damaged *Invisible Hand*.

OUTCOME:
Anakin steers the ship to a safe landing on Coruscant; Palpatine is safe. MISSION COMPLETE.

CONSEQUENCES

Following the Battle of Coruscant, the Separatists have lost both their flagship and their leader, Count Dooku. With General Grievous still on the loose, however, the Clone Wars are far from over. And Anakin will soon learn that Chancellor Palpatine is a Sith Lord who hopes to make him his apprentice.

WHAT USE IS ONE SMALL ASTROMECH DROID?

ASTROMECH DROIDS may not look like much, but they are proof that good things come in small packages! Anakin's droid, R2-D2, is good at getting himself and his friends out of trouble. During the Battle of Coruscant, he proves he is both smart and brave when he helps Anakin and Obi-Wan rescue Chancellor Palpatine. He also saves himself from super battle droids by starting a big oil fire.

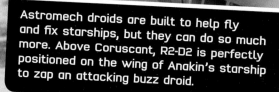

Astromech droids are built to help fly and fix starships, but they can do so much more. Above Coruscant, R2-D2 is perfectly positioned on the wing of Anakin's starship to zap an attacking buzz droid.

R2-D2 is useful if you don't know where you're going. He plugs in and downloads the blueprints of General Grievous's ship. Then his holoprojector shows Obi-Wan and Anakin the fastest path to the Chancellor.

R2's gadgets are great for creating a distraction! When Palpatine's rescue team is captured, the clever droid pops out all his arms and sprays fire-fighting foam. At first, the battle droids don't notice that he's cutting Obi-Wan loose—and when they do, it's too late!

HOW CAN A JEDI FIGHT WITHOUT A LIGHTSABER?

OBI-WAN KENOBI IS in trouble. He's been sent to Utapau to defeat Separatist cyborg General Grievous, but he drops his lightsaber during a bumpy ride on Boga, his varactyl steed. Grievous and his MagnaGuards are a threatening sight —are they too much for a Jedi with no lightsaber? Obi-Wan really needs to think of a way out of this one. Fast.

Obi-Wan isn't intimidated easily. Grievous might have a super-fast wheel bike, but Obi-Wan jumps onto Boga, who keeps up just fine. Obi-Wan grabs Grievous's electrostaff and attacks him with it, leaping onto the speeding bike.

Obi-Wan has enough Jedi wisdom to realize that a weapon is only as good as whoever holds it. Even though he thinks blasters are "uncivilized," Obi-Wan channels his Jedi skill into getting a clean shot at Grievous, and succeeds in destroying the villain.

DECOYS AND
Disguise

Charging into danger with blasters blazing is sometimes a guaranteed way to lose! Going undercover can be tricky, but it might be the best way to uncover carefully guarded secrets. Disguises can also come in handy when protecting important people from their enemies. If you need to don a sneaky disguise, here are some tried and tested tips.

2. BE INCONSPICUOUS

Stranded on Tatooine, Qui-Gon Jinn tries to blend in to avoid trouble. He conceals his lightsaber and Jedi clothing while he searches for a new hyperdrive for Queen Amidala's ship.

1. MIX IT UP

Queen Amidala of Naboo has many handmaidens. They are great bodyguards, but that's not all: They look so much like the Queen that any of them can take her place. When a handmaiden puts on the Queen's clothing and makeup, Amidala becomes a red-robed handmaiden. No one knows that the "Queen" is a decoy!

3. USE A DROID

Droids make excellent spies—as well as great hiding places! An astromech droid like R2-D2 can download and carry lots of information, and droids are so common that most people ignore them. R2 escapes with Princess Leia's message because the Imperials are too busy scanning for lifeforms to notice a droid.

4. BORROW A UNIFORM

Disguising yourself as a member of the enemy is almost always a good plan, especially if they wear armor and helmets that will help hide your identity. Aboard the Death Star, Luke Skywalker and Han Solo change into stormtrooper armor and walk straight into the detention center.

5. BE SNEAKY

Sometimes the best plans take shape at the last minute. Han Solo poses as an AT-ST driver when the Rebels can't get into the Empire's shield bunker. His gamble pays off when the back door is opened!

7. HIDE IN PLAIN SIGHT

Not even the Jedi realized that Chancellor Palpatine, ruler of the Republic, was really the Sith Lord Darth Sidious. By acting like he had nothing to hide, he hid the biggest secret of all. If you go undercover, make sure you keep calm and act confident at all times.

6. REALLY MEAN IT

Sometimes you need to go deep undercover. To infiltrate the heart of your enemy's stronghold, you must truly act the part. When Princess Leia poses as the bounty hunter Boushh, she plays the role of a tough criminal by threatening Jabba with a thermal detonator!

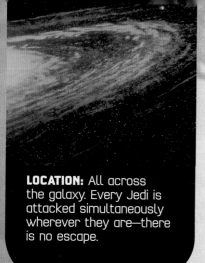

BATTLE ANALYSIS:
JEDI PURGE

LOCATION: All across the galaxy. Every Jedi is attacked simultaneously wherever they are—there is no escape.

Darth Sidious has been planning to destroy the Jedi for years, and as the Clone Wars come to an end he springs his trap! Because Sidious is also Chancellor Palpatine, the leader of the Republic, the clone troopers of the Republic army must obey his commands—they have been brainwashed to do so. He issues Order 66, which states that all Jedi are traitors to the Republic, and across the galaxy the troopers turn on their Jedi Generals and friends.

1. THE ORDER

OBJECTIVE:
Darth Sidious to activate Order 66 via hologram.

OUTCOME:
Across the galaxy, clone commanders receive the deadly instruction. MISSION COMPLETE.

2. UTAPAU

OBJECTIVE:
Clones to destroy all Jedi on Utapau.

OUTCOME:
Clones fire at Obi-Wan. He falls into a crater, but survives. MISSION FAILED.

3. MYGEETO

OBJECTIVE:
Clones to destroy all Jedi on Mygeeto.

OUTCOME:
Ki-Adi-Mundi is felled by his troops. MISSION COMPLETE.

4. FELUCIA

OBJECTIVE:
Clones to destroy all Jedi on Felucia.

OUTCOME:
Aayla Secura is shot in the back by her own soldiers. MISSION COMPLETE.

BATTLE STATS

CLONE ARMY:

- SITH
- CLONE TROOPERS
- BARC SPEEDERS
- ARC-170 STARFIGHTERS
- TURBO TANKS
- WEAPONS: BLASTERS

JEDI:

- JEDI
- DELTA-7 STARFIGHTERS
- 74-Z SPEEDERS
- WEAPONS: LIGHTSABERS

> "The time has come. Execute ORDER 66."
>
> **Darth Sidious**

5. KASHYYYK

OBJECTIVE:
Clones to destroy all Jedi on Kashyyyk.

OUTCOME:
Yoda senses danger. He fights the clones and escapes. MISSION FAILED.

6. SALEUCAMI

OBJECTIVE:
Clones to destroy all Jedi on Saleucami.

OUTCOME:
Clones blow up Stass Allie's speeder bike. MISSION COMPLETE.

7. CATO NEIMOIDIA

OBJECTIVE:
Clones to destroy all Jedi on Cato Neimoidia.

OUTCOME:
Clone pilots destroy Plo Koon's Jedi starfighter. MISSION COMPLETE.

CONSEQUENCES

The Jedi Purge leaves the Jedi Order defeated and the surviving Jedi are too few to stop Darth Sidious. The Sith Lord seizes control of the galaxy and names himself Emperor. After thousands of years of Jedi power, their fire has gone out of the universe. Dark days follow.

8. CORUSCANT

OBJECTIVE:
Darth Vader to wipe out all Jedi in the Jedi Temple.

OUTCOME:
Vader and a squad of clones massacre all the Jedi. MISSION COMPLETE.

MIGHTY WARRIOR

Tarfful is one of Chewbacca's oldest friends. When Kashyyyk is attacked, he steps up to defend his homeland. Taking charge of the defenses for Kachirho City, Tarfful is ready to show the droid army that the Wookiees are the best fighters in the galaxy.

SOME WOOKIEES HAVE HUNDREDS OF YEARS OF BATTLE EXPERIENCE

CHEWBACCA

CHEWBACCA IS A GOOD PILOT AND MECHANIC

TARFFUL

ARMOR PLATING DEFLECTS BLASTER FIRE

FORMIDABLE FORCE

Wookiees on the warpath have been known to pull people's arms from their sockets! They are nearly unstoppable when enraged, but always obey their city's war chieftain, Tarfful. During the Battle of Kashyyyk, Wookiees and clone troopers fight side by side.

WOOKIEE STATS

LEADER: KING GRAKCHAWWAA
ALLEGIANCE: REPUBLIC
HEADQUARTERS: KASHYYYK
WEAPONS: BOWCASTER, BLASTER, SLUG THROWER
VEHICLES: ORNITHOPTER, FLYING CATAMARAN
VALUES: SOCIETY, LOYALTY

FLUTTERING INTO ACTION

The Wookiee ornithopter is a lightweight flyer used for scouting. Like all Wookiee creations it is hand-crafted from local materials, unlike the factory-made war machines of the Separatists.

WOOKIEE BOWCASTER FIRES ENERGY BULLETS

Wookiees have deep family bonds and prefer to stay on their home planet, Kashyyyk. With help from Yoda and the Republic's clone troopers, they push back the invading battle droids.

HAIRY HERO

Loyal and brave, Chewbacca puts his bowcaster to good use during the Battle of Kashyyyk. He survives to fight another day and later battles against the Empire with his friend, Han Solo.

Wookiee ARMY

Wookiees may be strong and fierce, but they are also friendly creatures who live in harmony with nature. When the Separatists invade the planet Kashyyyk, they quickly learn that there's hardly anything more dangerous than an angry Wookiee!

CHAIN OF COMMAND

KING GRAKCHAWWAA

CITY WAR CHIEFTAIN TARFFUL

WOOKIEE WARRIORS

Clone Trooper to
STORMTROOPER

The helmet has a T-shaped visor that closely resembles the one worn by Jango Fett. It also has a fin on top.

The Clone Wars are over. The Republic is now an oppressive Empire and Chancellor Palpatine has taken control as Emperor. And he doesn't have to look far to find an army to do his bidding. With only a few modifications, the Republic's clone troopers are swiftly transformed into Imperial stormtroopers. Their mission may have changed from defeating Separatists to destroying Rebels, but these troopers have always stayed loyal to their commander.

Each trooper carries a standard issue DC-15A blaster rifle which can fire up to 500 shots on a single ammo pack.

JANGO FETT

This deadly bounty hunter caught the attention of Count Dooku, who hired him to be the source of the genetic material used to create the clones. Jango also helped train the clones, and their armor —especially the Phase I design— is clearly based on Jango's Mandalorian battle armor.

Rocket backpack also contains a missile

Gauntlet can spray fire at enemies

ORIGINS OF THE CLONE

Phase I armor is made up of a black bodysuit, surrounded by a 20-piece blaster-resistant shell. Commanders have yellow markings.

PHASE I CLONE TROOPER

Early clone troopers wear identical white armor—except for commanders, who have colored markings. This armor is bulky and uncomfortable for long-term combat.

The new helmet includes an advanced air filtration system, while the visor contains a targeting system and screen that displays important information.

The helmet is now fully sealed and can supply emergency air for 20 minutes. Some troopers complain about the smaller eyeholes.

The DC-15A blaster rifle is still in use, but troopers also carry special weapons if needed.

Stormtroopers carry the E-11 blaster rifle. On its automatic setting, it fires blaster bolts at an extremely high rate of speed.

This armor can survive explosions and blaster hits, and the foot casing can be magnetized. Phase II armor is easily personalized to denote unit affiliation, or painted in camouflage colors.

Stormtrooper armor consists of only 18 blaster-resistant pieces, surrounding a black bodysuit that can adapt to extreme temperatures.

PHASE II CLONE TROOPER

Battlefield experience in the Clone Wars leads to Phase II armor. It is more flexible and comfortable. Troopers often adapt or paint their armor for particular missions.

IMPERIAL STORMTROOPER

To symbolize the purity of the new Empire, stormtrooper armor returns to the all-white coloration of the earliest clones. The look inspires fear across the galaxy!

REVIEWING THE TROOPS

As the Emperor's right-hand man, Darth Vader outranks most officers. The Sith Lord has the power to command legions of stormtroopers and has his own ship—the Super Star Destroyer—*Executor*.

Stormtroopers are a special branch of the Imperial forces, and most of them are clones. The Imperial military also includes army and navy troopers, TIE fighter pilots, AT-AT drivers, and the Emperor's red-robed Royal Guard.

Imperial ARMY

The Empire has one of the most powerful militaries in the history of the galaxy. Well-equipped and well-trained, there are thousands of stormtroopers, starships, and vehicles ready to invade troublesome planets. The Imperial Army is confident it will crush the Rebellion soon.

CHAIN OF COMMAND

EMPEROR PALPATINE

GRAND MOFFS

GENERALS/ADMIRALS

IMPERIAL OFFICERS

STORMTROOPERS

CLONE TO STORM

Clone troopers became stormtroopers when the Clone Wars ended with Order 66. Specialty units such as snowtroopers, sandtroopers, and scout troopers are easily recognized by distinctive armor.

IMPERIAL STORMTROOPER

HELMET CONTAINS TARGETING EQUIPMENT

INSIGNIA SHOWS HIGH RANK

GRAND MOFF TARKIN

SUPERIOR

Grand Moff Tarkin is in charge of the Death Star project and has served the Emperor since the beginning. Cruel and power-hungry, he is one of the few Imperial officials with enough authority to give orders to Darth Vader!

REPUBLIC FIGHTER

The ARC-170 is a heavy starfighter often used as a bomber. It only takes an ARC-170, two pilots, a gunner, and an astromech droid to make enemies turn and run!

ASSAULT SHIPS

Some starfighters can do everything from bombing to dogfighting. Certain features of the Republic's ARC-170 were incorporated into the Rebel Alliance's famous X-wing.

REBEL FAVORITE

The X-wing is a sturdy one-pilot ship, but it still uses an astromech. It offers a good balance of speed and firepower, and is equipped with two proton torpedoes.

WARTIME TRANSFORMATION

War can destroy, but it can also create. In order to gain an edge over their enemies, armies invent new technologies and designs to improve their starships and ground vehicles. Between the final days of the Republic and the fall of the Empire, the vehicles of combat became better and better, even though their basic shapes remained the same.

REPUBLIC MACHINE

This six-legged AT-TE walker is difficult to knock over and can even climb up cliff faces. It is packed with weapons, but can be destroyed by enemy cannons.

HEAVY WALKERS

Clone troopers used walkers to smash Separatist tanks during the Clone Wars. The design worked so well that the Empire built its own deadly walkers.

IMPERIAL MONSTER

The fearsome AT-AT towers over other war machines. It is less stable than the AT-TE but much tougher and scarier.

REPUBLIC SCOUT

The AT-RT is a small scouting vehicle that gives its driver a high vantage point to scan the territory, but it also makes him an easy target.

SCOUT WALKERS

The Republic army used two-legged walkers for fast scouting of unfamiliar terrain. The Imperial Army improved the design by adding more protection for the walker's drivers.

IMPERIAL THREAT

The Imperial AT-ST is taller than the AT-RT and its cockpit is completely enclosed. It is better armed as well, so keep clear—for your own safety!

REPUBLIC STAR

The Jedi Interceptor carries an astromech droid and is so small and maneuverable that it's hard to hit! Due to its compact size, it needs a hyperspace ring for long-distance travel.

INTERCEPTORS

The Jedi Interceptor was small, lightweight, and fast. Some parts of its design were used in Imperial TIE fighters, while others were incorporated into the Rebel Alliance's trusty A-wing.

REBEL SPEEDSTER

The A-wing doesn't have an astromech droid, but it does have a built-in hyperdrive engine for quick escapes. Rebel pilots love its speed!

REPUBLIC POWER

The Republic Attack Cruiser carries starfighters, walkers, and up to 2,000 soldiers. It can land directly on planets to unload its troops while giving covering fire.

DESTROYERS

In the Clone Wars, these huge ships carried clone troops. After installing more weapons, the Empire used Star Destroyers to smash Rebel battleships and conquer entire planets.

IMPERIAL MIGHT

The Imperial Star Destroyer is bigger than the Attack Cruiser and can't land on planets. But it can destroy targets from space with its turbolasers— and it carries squadrons of TIE fighters.

JEDI CONNECTION
WITH THE FORCE

X-WING ACE

Luke Skywalker is one of the Alliance's best pilots, thanks to his Jedi skills. Luke's belief in freedom and justice is so strong that he does not sway in his dedication to the Rebellion, even when he discovers that Darth Vader is his father.

INSULATED,
AIRTIGHT
FLIGHT SUIT

REBEL STATS

LEADER: MON MOTHMA
ALLEGIANCE: REBEL ALLIANCE
HEADQUARTERS: MOBILE
WEAPONS: DH-17 BLASTER PISTOL, A280 BLASTER RIFLE, PROTON GRENADE
VEHICLES: X-WING, Y-WING, SNOWSPEEDER, B-WING, A-WING, MON CALAMARI CRUISER
VALUES: JUSTICE, FREEDOM

PRINCESS LEIA

LUKE SKYWALKER

AMBASSADOR

Like her brother Luke, Princess Leia is a committed Rebel. She would rather negotiate than fight, but is quick to defend herself if stormtroopers threaten!

SPORTING
BLASTER PISTOL

AMBASSADOR'S
ROBES ARE
TREATED WITH
RESPECT ON
MOST WORLDS

CHAIN OF COMMAND

MON MOTHMA

REBEL GENERALS/ADMIRALS

REBEL OFFICERS

REBEL TROOPERS

ALLIANCE LEADERS

Mon Mothma, the senator from Chandrila, commands all the Rebel forces. Before each mission she meets with her Generals and Admirals to get their advice.

ADMIRAL ACKBAR

The navy is the backbone of the Rebel military. Admiral Ackbar and his people, the Mon Calamari, supply huge warships that can stand up to Imperial Star Destroyers. Ackbar is a brilliant commander who doesn't like to take foolish risks.

The brave soldiers of the Rebel Alliance join together to defeat the Empire or die trying! Based in secret hideouts and using patched-together equipment, these hopeful volunteers must stay one step ahead of Darth Vader and the mighty

Rebel ALLIANCE

THE REBELS

The Rebels have to make do with whatever vehicles they can get, even when they're as unreliable as the *Millennium Falcon* can be! But, like the *Falcon*, Rebel ships pack a powerful punch. Ace pilots love the speedy X-wing and other starfighters, while big ships like Mon Calamari Cruisers can stand up to powerful Imperial Star Destroyers.

B-WING
- **SIZE** 16.9 m (55.4 ft) TALL
- **MAX ACCELERATION** 2,390 G
- **CAPACITY** 1 PILOT (PLUS 1 GUNNER IN SPECIAL MODELS)
- **WEAPONS** 3 ION CANNONS, 1 HEAVY LASER CANNON, 1 TWIN BLASTER, 2 TORPEDO LAUNCHERS

A-WING
- **SIZE** 9.6 m (31.5 ft) LONG
- **MAX ACCELERATION** 5,100 G
- **CAPACITY** 1 PILOT
- **WEAPONS** 2 LASER CANNONS, 2 MISSILE LAUNCHERS

NEBULON-B FRIGATE
- **SIZE** 300 m (984 ft) LONG
- **MAX ACCELERATION** 1,200 G
- **CAPACITY** 920 CREW, 75 PASSENGERS
- **WEAPONS** 12 TURBOLASERS, 12 LASER CANNONS, 2 TRACTOR BEAM PROJECTORS

SPACE

REBEL TRANSPORT
- **SIZE** 90 m (295 ft) LONG
- **MAX ACCELERATION** 900 G
- **CAPACITY** 7 CREW, 90 PASSENGERS
- **WEAPONS** 4 TWIN LASER TURRETS

Y-WING
- **SIZE** 16 m (52.5 ft) LONG
- **MAX ACCELERATION** 2,700 G
- **CAPACITY** 1 PILOT (PLUS 1 GUNNER IN SPECIAL MODELS)
- **WEAPONS** 2 LASER CANNONS, 2 ION CANNONS, 2 TORPEDO LAUNCHERS, PROTON BOMB

MON CALAMARI CRUISER
- **SIZE** 1,200 m (3,937 ft) LONG
- **MAX ACCELERATION** 2,750 G
- **CAPACITY** 5,400 CREW, 1,200 TROOPERS
- **WEAPONS** 48 TURBOLASERS, 20 ION CANNONS, 6 TRACTOR BEAM PROJECTORS

REBEL BLOCKADE RUNNER
- **SIZE** 150 m (492 ft) LONG
- **MAX ACCELERATION** 2,100 G
- **CAPACITY** 100 CREW, 600 PASSENGERS
- **WEAPONS** 2 TWIN TURBOLASERS, 4 SINGLE TURBOLASERS

MILLENNIUM FALCON
- **SIZE** 34.75 m (114 ft) LONG
- **MAX ACCELERATION** 3,000 G
- **CAPACITY** 2 PILOTS, 2 GUNNERS
- **WEAPONS** 2 QUAD LASER CANNONS, 1 CONCEALED BLASTER CANNON, 2 MISSILE LAUNCHERS

ASTROMECH DROID SOCKET

EXCELLENT STABILITY FOR STARFIGHTER DOGFIGHTS

LASERS FIRE SEPARATELY OR ALL AT ONCE

S-FOIL WINGS FOLD OUT FOR COMBAT

CARRIES UP TO 6 PROTON TORPEDOES

X-WING
- **SIZE** 12.5 m (41 ft) LONG
- **MAX ACCELERATION** 3,700 G
- **CAPACITY** 1 PILOT
- **WEAPONS** 4 LASER CANNONS, 2 TORPEDO LAUNCHERS

AIR

HARPOON GUN FIRES FUSION DISK ATTACHED TO TOW CABLE

CANNOT SURVIVE FULL-FORCE HOTH SNOWSTORM

ENGINES MODIFIED FOR COLD WEATHER

SNOWSPEEDER
- **SIZE** 5.3 m (17.4 ft) LONG
- **SPEED** 1,100 km/hr (684 mph)
- **CAPACITY** 1 PILOT, 1 GUNNER
- **WEAPONS** 2 LASER CANNONS, 1 HARPOON GUN

LASER CANNONS LINKED TO FIRE SIMULTANEOUSLY

FLIES UP TO 175 KM (107 MILES) ABOVE GROUND

TARGET: THE DEATH STAR

Rebel soldiers, it is time for action! But before going into battle, you must study your target. The Death Star is the biggest Imperial battle station ever built, and each part has a different function. Study the Death Star plans we have captured from our enemies so you can sneak into the Empire's base to rescue prisoners—or even destroy it from within.

Do not be fooled by a battle station that looks incomplete. The second Imperial Death Star might be fully operational, despite its appearance.

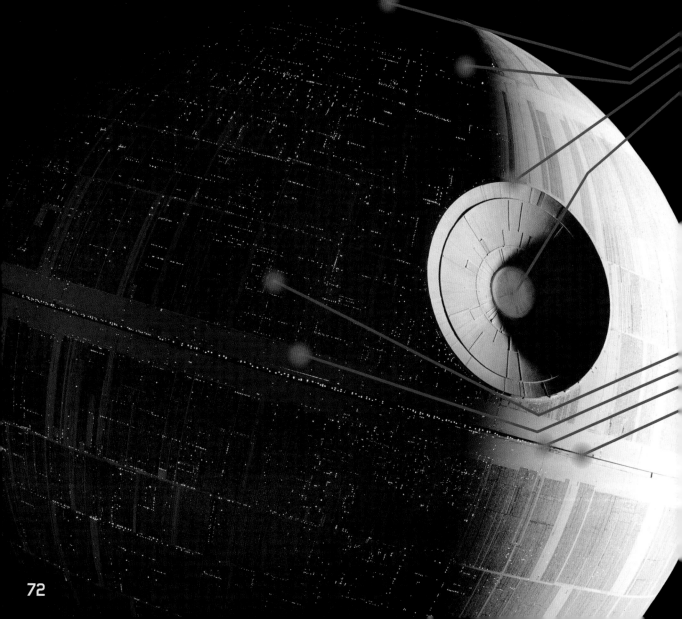

Many Death Star systems are run by droids instead of humans. A smart Rebel droid could locate the control room, plug into the Imperial computer bank, and access top-secret data.

Decisions concerning Imperial warfare are made inside conference rooms like this one. Generals, Admirals, and Grand Moffs are some of the most important people in the Empire's upper ranks.

The Death Star is so important it even contains a grand throne room for the Emperor, should he choose to visit. The throne room sits in a tower at the station's north pole.

The Death Star's powerful superlaser combines several energy beams into a single blast that smashes planets to smithereens.

Docking bays at the Death Star's equator hold TIE fighters and captured freighters. The bay is open to space and a magnetic force-field holds the air inside.

If they survive capture, Rebels might be held prisoner in one of the Death Star's detention bays. The jail cells are cold and uncomfortable—and supposedly escape-proof.

During a starfighter attack against the Death Star, you will need to watch out for the station's turbolasers. Hopefully the compact Rebel fighters will be too small and quick for the targeting systems of the big guns.

Empty shafts lead down in the direction of the Death Star's reactor core. Tractor beam controls and other systems can be hard to reach, so watch your step!

"FEAR WILL KEEP THE LOCAL SYSTEMS IN LINE. FEAR OF THIS BATTLE STATION."
GRAND MOFF TARKIN

HOW CAN A PRINCESS RESCUE HERSELF?

PRINCESS LEIA ISN'T afraid of anything. She is determined to bring down the Empire and her bold, fearless actions sometimes get her into trouble. But this is one princess who doesn't sit around waiting to be rescued. Leia's take-charge attitude usually saves her—and others.

Luke, Han, and Chewie free Leia from the Death Star's jail, but the princess quickly takes command. Picking up a stormtrooper's blaster, she clears a path to freedom.

Jabba the Hutt is the galaxy's worst gangster, and chaining Princess Leia to his throne is his last mistake. Leia uses the chain as a weapon to bring Jabba's evil rule to an end.

MISSION DATA

■ Princess Leia is the daughter of Anakin Skywalker and is strong in the Force. Although she hasn't been trained as a Jedi, she is a tough fighter and a smart negotiator.

BATTLE ANALYSIS:
YAVIN

PLANET: Yavin 4

LOCATION: Outer Rim Territories

TERRAIN: Jungle, ancient ruins, Rebel headquarters

INHABITANTS: Rebel Alliance soldiers

ALLEGIANCE: Rebel Alliance

The Emperor's Death Star has tracked the Rebels to their headquarters on the jungle moon of Yavin 4. The battle station's superlaser can blast the moon to rubble and will be ready to fire in only minutes. The Rebels have only one chance: If a starfighter can evade TIE fighters and hit the Death Star's tiny exhaust port, the station will explode. As the Rebel pilots board their ships, they know that they will either triumph—or die!

1. DEATH STAR APPROACH

OBJECTIVE:
Red and Gold Squadrons to weaken the Death Star's defences.

OUTCOME:
The Death Star's ion cannons and communications centers are taken out. MISSION COMPLETE.

2. SPACE BATTLE

OBJECTIVE:
Rebel pilots to wipe out Imperial TIE fighters.

OUTCOME:
During fast-paced combat both sides take losses. MISSION FAILED.

BATTLE STATS

EMPIRE:
- SITH
- IMPERIAL TROOPS AND STAFF
- DEATH STAR
- TIE FIGHTERS
- TIE ADVANCED X1

REBEL ALLIANCE:
- STAR PILOTS
- T-65 X-WINGS
- BTL Y-WINGS
- *MILLENNIUM FALCON*

> # "Great shot, kid, that was one in a million!"

Han Solo to Luke Skywalker

3. FIRST TRENCH RUN

OBJECTIVE:
Gold Squadron's Y-wings to hit the Death Star's thermal exhaust port.

....

OUTCOME:
Y-wings destroyed by Darth Vader. MISSION FAILED.

4. SECOND TRENCH RUN

OBJECTIVE:
Red Squadron's X-wings to hit the thermal exhaust port.

....

OUTCOME:
X-wings fire but miss, and are destroyed by Darth Vader. MISSION FAILED.

5. DARTH VADER

OBJECTIVE:
Millennium Falcon to attack Darth Vader.

....

OUTCOME:
Han Solo damages Vader's TIE fighter, allowing Luke to fire. MISSION COMPLETE.

6. FINAL CHANCE

CONSEQUENCES

The Battle of Yavin is a triumph for the Rebel Alliance, but they know that the Empire will soon strike back. The Rebels leave Yavin behind and build a new secret base on the frozen planet of Hoth. Luke Skywalker and Han Solo receive medals for their heroism and stay to help the Rebels in their fight.

OBJECTIVE:
Luke Skywalker to destroy the Death Star.

OUTCOME:
Luke uses the Force to strike the exhaust port, and blows up the Death Star. MISSION COMPLETE.

night be gone, but
n in the Force. Luke
tion with the Force
s advice. He turns
computer and
cts.

AT IS THE
OWER OF
E FORCE?

THE FORCE IS A mystical energy field, and both the Jedi and the Sith can tap into it. It is extremely powerful and, if you know how to channel it, you can change the course of an entire battle. At the Battle of Yavin, both Luke Skywalker and Darth Vader use the Force to sharpen their focus and skill at high-speed piloting. But who will triumph in the end?

Luke calls on the Force to help guide his shot to the small target, and the proton torpedoes score a direct hit! The Death Star explodes, and as Luke flies away he hears Obi-Wan's voice: "The Force will be with you, always."

THE EMPIRE

The Empire's starships and vehicles are designed to make enemies run in terror! The mighty AT-AT walker shakes the ground as it moves and TIE fighter engines make an eerie wailing sound. Smaller Imperial vehicles are used for scouting and patrolling, while high-ranking officers travel in style aboard Star Destroyers and luxury Imperial Shuttles.

ALL TERRAIN ARMORED TRANSPORT (AT-AT)
- **SIZE** 22.5 m (73.8 ft) TALL
- **SPEED** 60 km/hr (37 mph)
- **CAPACITY** 3 CREW, 40 TROOPERS
- **WEAPONS** 2 HEAVY LASER CANNONS, 2 MEDIUM BLASTER CANNONS

ALL TERRAIN SCOUT TRANSPORT (AT-ST)
- **SIZE** 8.6 m (28.2 ft) TALL
- **SPEED** 90 km/hr (56 mph)
- **CAPACITY** 1 PILOT, 1 GUNNER
- **WEAPONS** 2 TWIN BLASTER CANNONS, 1 GRENADE LAUNCHER

COMMANDERS HAVE GOOD VIEW OF BATTLEFIELD

HEAVY ARMOR WITHSTANDS BLASTER FIRE

LEGS GIVE EXCELLENT MOVEMENT OVER UNEVEN SURFACES

HUGE FEET CRUSH ENEMIES

LAND

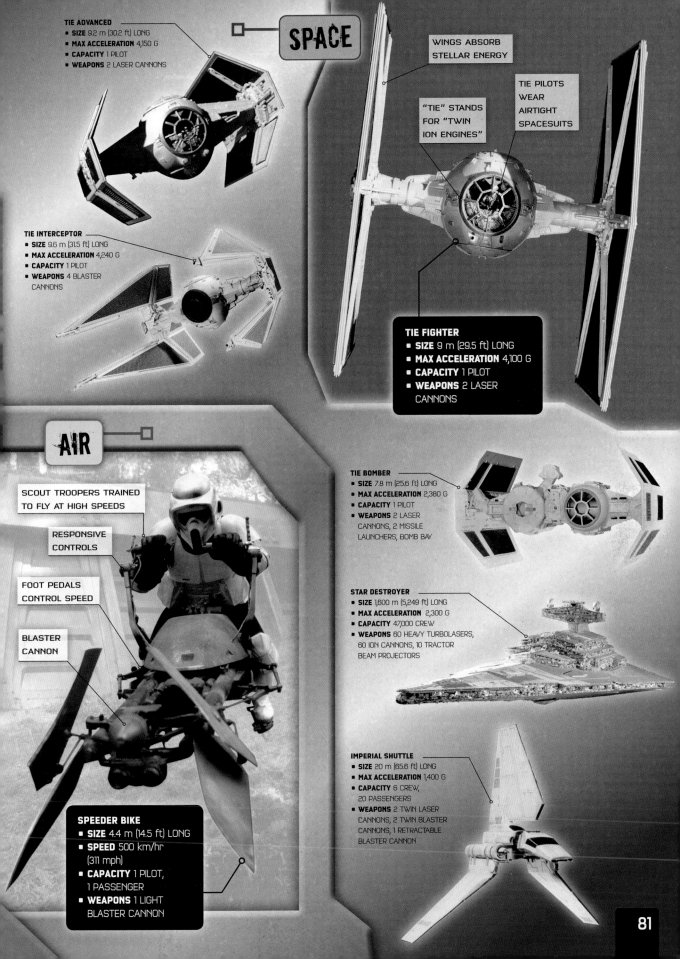

TIE ADVANCED
- **SIZE** 9.2 m (30.2 ft) LONG
- **MAX ACCELERATION** 4,150 G
- **CAPACITY** 1 PILOT
- **WEAPONS** 2 LASER CANNONS

WINGS ABSORB STELLAR ENERGY

"TIE" STANDS FOR "TWIN ION ENGINES"

TIE PILOTS WEAR AIRTIGHT SPACESUITS

TIE INTERCEPTOR
- **SIZE** 9.6 m (31.5 ft) LONG
- **MAX ACCELERATION** 4,240 G
- **CAPACITY** 1 PILOT
- **WEAPONS** 4 BLASTER CANNONS

TIE FIGHTER
- **SIZE** 9 m (29.5 ft) LONG
- **MAX ACCELERATION** 4,100 G
- **CAPACITY** 1 PILOT
- **WEAPONS** 2 LASER CANNONS

AIR

SCOUT TROOPERS TRAINED TO FLY AT HIGH SPEEDS

RESPONSIVE CONTROLS

FOOT PEDALS CONTROL SPEED

BLASTER CANNON

TIE BOMBER
- **SIZE** 7.8 m (25.6 ft) LONG
- **MAX ACCELERATION** 2,380 G
- **CAPACITY** 1 PILOT
- **WEAPONS** 2 LASER CANNONS, 2 MISSILE LAUNCHERS, BOMB BAY

STAR DESTROYER
- **SIZE** 1,600 m (5,249 ft) LONG
- **MAX ACCELERATION** 2,300 G
- **CAPACITY** 47,000 CREW
- **WEAPONS** 60 HEAVY TURBOLASERS, 60 ION CANNONS, 10 TRACTOR BEAM PROJECTORS

SPEEDER BIKE
- **SIZE** 4.4 m (14.5 ft) LONG
- **SPEED** 500 km/hr (311 mph)
- **CAPACITY** 1 PILOT, 1 PASSENGER
- **WEAPONS** 1 LIGHT BLASTER CANNON

IMPERIAL SHUTTLE
- **SIZE** 20 m (65.6 ft) LONG
- **MAX ACCELERATION** 1,400 G
- **CAPACITY** 6 CREW, 20 PASSENGERS
- **WEAPONS** 2 TWIN LASER CANNONS, 2 TWIN BLASTER CANNONS, 1 RETRACTABLE BLASTER CANNON

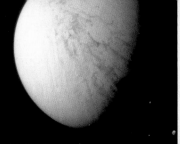

HOTH

PLANET: Hoth

LOCATION: A remote sector of the Outer Rim Territories

TERRAIN: Glaciers, snow fields

INHABITANTS: Rebel Alliance soldiers, wampa ice monsters

ALLEGIANCE: Rebel Alliance

The Rebel Alliance has found a remote hideout for their new base. However, they know it's only a matter of time until the Empire tracks them down on the ice planet Hoth. The Rebels cannot win a battle against the better equipped Imperial troops, but they hope that they can hold off the Empire long enough to evacuate everyone on Echo Base to safety so they can live to fight another day.

"Imperial troops have entered the base!"
Rebel Trooper

2. EVACUATION

OBJECTIVE:
All non-military personnel to escape Hoth.

OUTCOME:
Rebel transports jump into hyperspace. MISSION COMPLETE.

1. PROBE DROID

OBJECTIVE:
Rebels to keep Echo Base hidden from the Empire.

OUTCOME:
Imperial probe droid spotted! Alarm is raised and evacuation begins. MISSION FAILED.

3. SNOW BATTLE

OBJECTIVE:
Rebel infantry and snowspeeders to delay the invading Imperial troops.

OUTCOME:
Rebels destroy some AT-ATs, but can't stop them all. MISSION INCOMPLETE.

4. SHIELD GENERATOR

OBJECTIVE:
Rebels to protect Echo Base's shield generator from Imperial attack.

OUTCOME:
An AT-AT blows up the generator, allowing more Imperial troops to land. MISSION FAILED.

BATTLE STATS

EMPIRE:
- STAR DESTROYERS
- AT-ATS
- IMPERIAL OFFICERS AND SNOWTROOPERS
- WEAPONS: BLASTER RIFLES, AT-AT CHIN GUNS

REBEL ALLIANCE:
- DF.9 ANTI-INFANTRY BATTERIES
- P-TOWER LASER CANNONS
- T-47 AIRSPEEDERS
- REBEL GENERALS AND TROOPERS
- WEAPONS: BLASTER RIFLES

5. ECHO BASE

OBJECTIVE:
Rebel troops to prevent Imperial snowtroopers from capturing the base.

OUTCOME:
Darth Vader and his troopers quickly take control. MISSION FAILED.

6. ESCAPE

OBJECTIVE:
All remaining Rebels to abandon Echo Base and the Hoth system.

OUTCOME:
X-wings, transports, and the *Millennium Falcon* escape the battle. MISSION COMPLETE.

CONSEQUENCES

The Rebels escape after the Battle of Hoth, but they are badly hurt and weakened. Scattered and on the run from Imperial Star Destroyers, they regroup in deep space to plan their next move. The Empire looks stronger than ever, but the Rebels aren't discouraged. When the next battle comes, they will be ready!

The snowspeeder's gunner fires a tow cable and the pilot loops his ship around the AT-AT's legs. Careful flying is needed or the snowspeeder might accidentally crash into the walking war machine!

HOW CAN YOU STOP AN AT-AT IN ITS TRACKS?

THE EMPIRE'S AT-AT WALKERS can destroy the Rebels with their blaster cannons and crush any survivors underneath their mechanical feet. The defending snowspeeders can't make a scratch in the walkers' heavy armor. It looks bad until Luke Skywalker comes up with a smart but risky idea—AT-ATs are giant-sized, but even the mightiest giant can topple and fall!

Its legs tangled, the AT-AT topples forward and crashes! A snowspeeder pilot takes aim at the damaged walker and hits a weak point in its neck. With a roar of fire the Imperial walker explodes, giving the Rebels more time to escape their base.

EXPLORING
REBEL BASES

The life of a Rebel soldier is an uncertain one. The Rebel Alliance can't match the Empire's firepower, so it needs to keep one step ahead of the enemy and be ready to escape at any time—day or night. The Alliance has already been forced to abandon its bases on Yavin 4 and Hoth, and now operates from the Mon Calamari Cruiser *Home One*—which uses hyperspace to stay on the move.

As a new Rebel recruit, it is crucial that you familiarize yourself with the layout of your base. You must learn every escape route—so you are prepared for an emergency evacuation.

YAVIN 4
ABANDONED

Yavin 4 had many stone temples built by an ancient people called the Massassi. These pyramid-like structures were a good place to hide Rebel hangars and control rooms.

Technicians at the Yavin base constantly scanned the system for Imperial activity. They also worked hard to keep the X-wings and Y-wings in good condition in the jungle heat.

ECHO BASE: NEW RECRUITS MAP

NORTH
ENTRANCE

X-WING AND
AIRSPEEDER BAY

WELCOME TO ECHO BASE. IMPORTANT LOCATIONS HAVE BEEN FLAGGED ON THE MAP. IF YOU HAVE ANY QUESTIONS I CAN BE FOUND IN THE CENTRAL COMMAND ROOM.
GOOD LUCK, SOLDIER

Major Kem Monnon

ECHO BASE
ABANDONED

The Echo Base hangar on Hoth was carved from solid ice. The Rebel speeders needed modification so they could operate in freezing temperatures.

Top Alliance officers are always scheduling meetings to plan military strategy. Rebel soldiers must never be captured, so you can never let your guard down.

Every Rebel base needs a medical center. Bacta tanks and surgical droids can heal most injuries and get Rebel soldiers back to the front lines.

TOP SECRET: PRIORITY 4-B

CENTRAL COMMAND AND CONTROL ROOM

MEDICAL BAY

SOUTH ENTRANCE

BRIEFING AND HOLOPROJECTOR ROOM

MESS HALL

BARRACKS

1646278d9266291-267-992

HOME ONE
ACTIVE

Home One is the new mobile Rebel headquarters. It is protected by shields and turbolasers and it never stays in one place for long. In the briefing room, Imperial targets are displayed on holograms while soldiers and pilots receive their mission assignments.

CHAIN OF COMMAND

VILLAGE CHIEFTAIN (CHIEF CHIRPA)

COUNCIL OF ELDERS

WAR CHIEFS

EWOK WARRIORS

UNLIKELY FRIENDS

Visitors to Endor's moon are rare, and Ewoks are suspicious of outsiders. At first, they try to cook Han and Luke for dinner, but the Ewoks soon realize that the Rebels can help them keep their village safe from worse strangers.

In the dense forest of Endor, the Ewoks have a military advantage over the invading stormtroopers. They know every part of the terrain like the back of their paws, and they blend in with the forest colors.

Ewok WARRIORS

Ewoks may be small and furry, but watch out—these proud creatures can be fierce. The Ewoks don't know anything about the Galactic Civil War, but they do know that Imperial stormtroopers aren't welcome on their forest moon!

EWOK STATS

LEADER: CHIEF CHIRPA

ALLEGIANCE: REBEL ALLIANCE

HEADQUARTERS: BRIGHT TREE VILLAGE, MOON OF ENDOR

WEAPONS: CATAPULTS, LOG TRAPS, SNARES, ARROWS, SPEARS, BOLAS

VEHICLES: HANG GLIDERS, WAR WAGONS

VALUES: TRIBAL LOYALTY, PRESERVING NATURE

FIREPOWER

Ewok weapons and equipment made of wood, rope, and animal skins may look primitive, but with teamwork, the Ewoks are smart enough to defeat stormtroopers.

WISE LEADER

Chief Chirpa is the leader of the Ewoks who are drawn into war when their moon is chosen as the site for the Death Star's shield generator. Chirpa might not lead a trained army, but his tribe are brave, fierce, and determined to protect their home from the Empire.

HOODS ARE A SIGN OF ADULTHOOD

CHIEF CHIRPA

CHIRPA BELIEVES THAT HIS MEDALLION HAS MYSTICAL POWERS

CEREMONIAL KNIFE IS A SYMBOL OF HIGH RANK

WICKET W. WARRICK

WICKET'S FAVORITE WEAPONS ARE THE SPEAR AND THE BOLA

INQUISITIVE SCOUT

Wicket is a scout who gets more than he expects when he finds Princess Leia in the forest. His curiosity is matched by his bravery in the Battle of Endor.

89

MOON: Endor

LOCATION: A remote sector of the Outer Rim Territories

TERRAIN: Thick forests, treetop villages

INHABITANTS: Ewoks

ALLEGIANCE: None

BATTLE ANALYSIS:
ENDOR

After the Death Star is destroyed at the Battle of Yavin, the Empire builds a bigger, more powerful one! The Rebels plan to shut it down forever, but the battle station is protected by a shield, powered by a generator on the moon of Endor. A strike team lands on Endor to demolish the generator. Meanwhile, Lando Calrissian is standing by in the *Millennium Falcon*, waiting to attack the Death Star.

1. CAPTURED

OBJECTIVE:
Han Solo, Princess Leia, and Chewbacca to destroy the shield generator.

OUTCOME:
The trio realize they have walked into a trap and are captured. MISSION FAILED.

BATTLE STATS

EMPIRE:

- SITH
- IMPERIAL OFFICERS AND STORMTROOPERS
- DEATH STAR
- STAR DESTROYERS
- AT-STS

REBEL ALLIANCE:

- JEDI
- EWOK WARRIORS
- REBEL TROOPS
- MON CALAMARI CRUISERS
    - BTL Y-WINGS
    - T-65 X-WINGS
    - A-WINGS
    - B-WINGS
    - *MILLENNIUM FALCON*

2. SPACE BATTLE

OBJECTIVE:
Rebels to defeat Imperial warships near the Death Star.

OUTCOME:
Rebels destroy Imperial ships but take heavy losses too. MISSION INCOMPLETE.

3. LAND BATTLE

OBJECTIVE:
Rebels to fight their way out of the Imperial trap.

OUTCOME:
Ewoks join the fight and beat the soldiers with spears and rocks. MISSION COMPLETE.

4. DEATH STAR DUEL

OBJECTIVE:
Luke Skywalker to defeat Darth Vader and the Emperor.

OUTCOME:
Darth Vader throws the Emperor into a shaft to save Luke. MISSION COMPLETE.

> "The shield is down! Commence attack on the Death Star's **MAIN REACTOR.**"
>
> Admiral Ackbar

5. SHIELD GENERATOR

OBJECTIVE:
Strike team to destroy the shield protecting the Death Star.

OUTCOME:
This time, the generator explodes. MISSION COMPLETE.

6. DESTROY DEATH STAR

OBJECTIVE:
Lando to trigger an explosion in the Death Star's main reactor.

OUTCOME:
With the shield down, Lando blasts the core. MISSION COMPLETE.

CONSEQUENCES

The Battle of Endor is a great victory for the Rebel Alliance and the people of the galaxy. Celebrations are held from Coruscant to Tatooine to cheer the end of the Empire and the start of a new era of peace. Luke Skywalker is the last of the Jedi, but he can now re-establish the Jedi Order.

HOW CAN A SMALL ARMY TAKE ON THE EMPIRE?

ARMED ONLY WITH logs and rope, the Ewoks are up against the strongest army in the galaxy! But the Imperial Army is on unfamiliar ground, so when C-3PO leads them into an ambush, the clever little Ewoks show why they should never be underestimated!

A distracted enemy is a weakened enemy! A sneaky Ewok warrior steals a speeder bike and leads Imperial scout troopers on a wild chase. Now there are fewer guards at the Rebels' real target—the shield generator bunker.

The Ewoks might not have sophisticated weapons, but they know how to fight in a forest. Their catapults can dent AT-ST armor, and rolling logs can make the walkers slip and fall. And two tree trunks, released at just the right moment, can crush an AT-ST like an egg!

MISSION DATA

■ The Empire knew about the Ewoks when it chose Endor as the location of the new Death Star project, but it believed Ewoks were too small and simple to be a threat.

A lifelong gambler, Lando knows when to stand and when to walk away. Admiral Ackbar wants to retreat, but Lando suggests fighting the Star Destroyers to buy more time.

HOW DO YOU TURN AROUND A LOSING BATTLE?

IT'S A TRAP! The Rebel Alliance's sneak attack has failed and Imperial forces are now battle ready. The Rebels are vastly outnumbered both in space and on the moon of Endor. It looks hopeless. But Lando Calrissian has faith in his friends; working together, the Rebels still have a chance to bring down the Empire.

Lando never doubts that Han Solo and his team will destroy the Death Star's shield generator. When news of their success on Endor's moon comes through, Lando's delaying strategy pays off and the real attack on the now vulnerable Death Star begins!

SMALL BATTLES
CAN MAKE A BIG DIFFERENCE

What causes the Empire's defeat? In the end, it is a son's love for his father. Luke Skywalker never gives up hope, and he convinces Darth Vader to turn back to the light side of the Force. Like a row of falling dominoes, this compassionate act leads to the defeat of the Emperor and freedom for the entire galaxy.

LUKE SKYWALKER ESCAPES
Luke defeats Vader in a lightsaber duel, but the battle isn't over! The Emperor tries to turn Luke to the dark side, but Luke's willpower is strong and he resists.

DEATH OF AN EMPEROR

Furious, the Emperor fires Force lightning at Luke. Vader sees his son in pain and comes to his rescue. With his last bit of strength, Vader throws his Master into a deep pit.

THE EMPIRE'S COLLAPSE

Without their leader, everything goes wrong for the Imperial forces. Rebel starfighters take down the Empire's Super Star Destroyer and a ground team on Endor blows up the shield generator. Soon, the mighty Death Star suffers a critical hit to its main reactor and explodes.

THE SITH ARE DESTROYED

Now that the Emperor is dead and Darth Vader has turned away from the dark side of the Force, the Sith no longer rule the galaxy. Luke Skywalker can now turn the Jedi Order into the guardians of peace and justice once more.

THE RETURN OF ANAKIN SKYWALKER

Luke always believed that deep down, Darth Vader still had the good spirit of Anakin Skywalker. Vader is dying from his injuries but he is at peace. He tells Luke, "You were right about me."

REBEL ALLIANCE VICTORY

Across the galaxy, planets celebrate the Empire's downfall. For the Rebels it has been a long, hard fight, but by working together they have triumphed!

...THE JEDI ORDER LIVES ON...

97

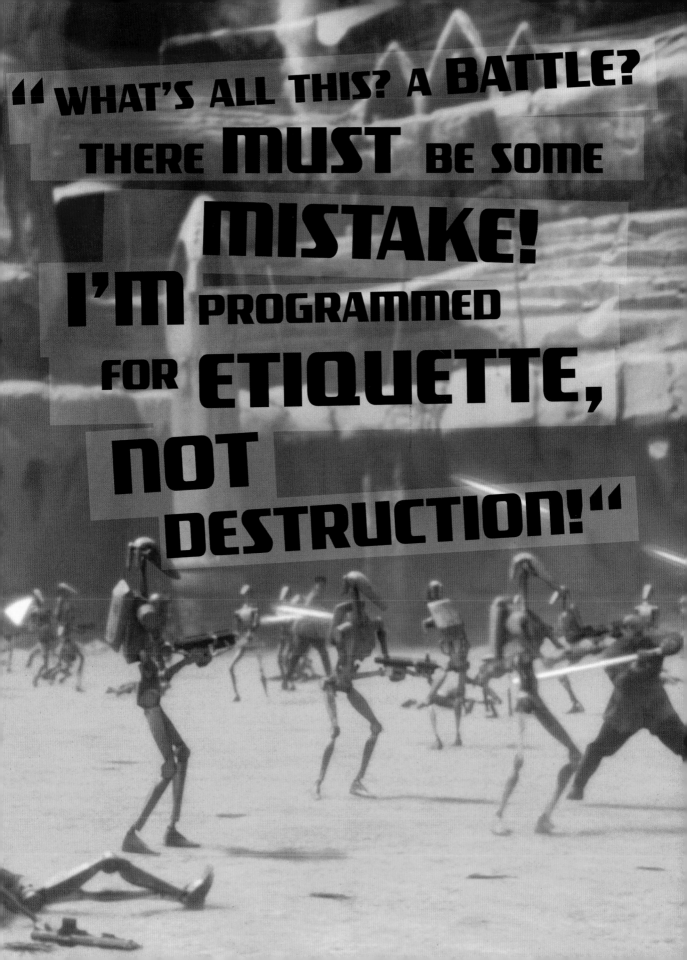

DROIDS

The galaxy is home to droids of all shapes and sizes. Some are friendly and high-functioning, while others are dull and simple. Droids live and work together with millions of living beings—but what makes them different from life-forms?

- **BUILT**

- **PROGRAMMED WITH SKILLS**

- **REPAIRED EASILY**

- **CAN'T SENSE THE FORCE**

MADE TO SERVE

Droids are built in factories and programmed to serve a particular function. Few ever learn to think of themselves as individuals because they often have their experiences erased by a memory wipe.

LIFE-FORMS

BORN ■

MUST LEARN SKILLS ■

HEAL SLOWLY ■

CAN SENSE ■
THE FORCE

BORN TO DREAM
Most life-forms are born
knowing very little, and
spend years learning
and forming memories.
Most think about the
future, and make choices
to decide what they
will accomplish during
their lives.

WHAT ABOUT CLONES?
The Republic's clone troopers
are living beings, but they
share some similarities with
droids. They are created in vats,
age more quickly than ordinary
humans, and their brains have
been manipulated to make them
good soldiers. Some life-forms
think of clones as living droids.

Types of DROID

LABOR

Labor droids are the most common type of droid. They include simple workers as well as sophisticated specialists.

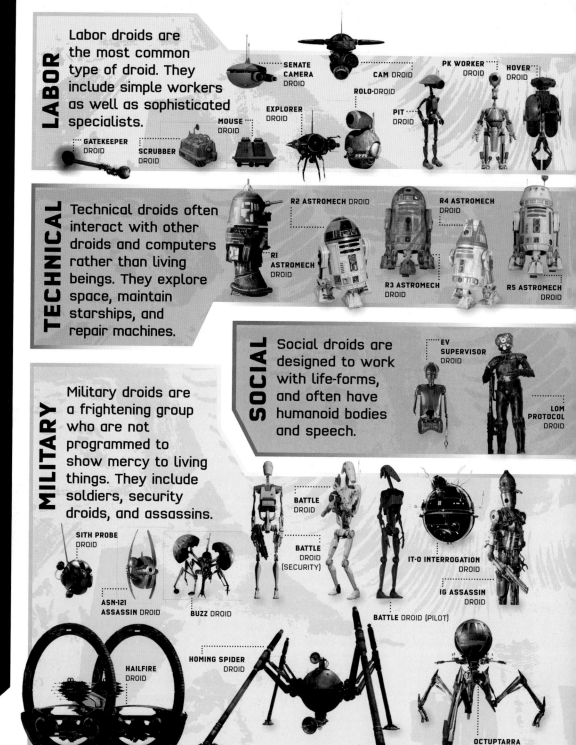

SENATE CAMERA DROID

CAM DROID

ROLO-DROID

PK WORKER DROID

HOVER DROID

EXPLORER DROID

PIT DROID

MOUSE DROID

GATEKEEPER DROID

SCRUBBER DROID

TECHNICAL

Technical droids often interact with other droids and computers rather than living beings. They explore space, maintain starships, and repair machines.

R1 ASTROMECH DROID

R2 ASTROMECH DROID

R4 ASTROMECH DROID

R3 ASTROMECH DROID

R5 ASTROMECH DROID

SOCIAL

Social droids are designed to work with life-forms, and often have humanoid bodies and speech.

EV SUPERVISOR DROID

LOM PROTOCOL DROID

MILITARY

Military droids are a frightening group who are not programmed to show mercy to living things. They include soldiers, security droids, and assassins.

SITH PROBE DROID

BATTLE DROID

BATTLE DROID (SECURITY)

IT-O INTERROGATION DROID

IG ASSASSIN DROID

ASN-121 ASSASSIN DROID

BUZZ DROID

BATTLE DROID (PILOT)

HAILFIRE DROID

HOMING SPIDER DROID

OCTUPTARRA DROID

SCIENCE/MEDICAL

Scientific droids have highly advanced programming. Medical droids are designed to interact with life-forms, but other scientific droids rarely do.

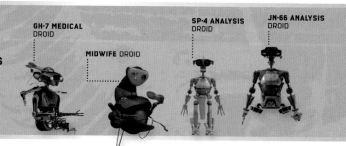

GH-7 MEDICAL DROID

MIDWIFE DROID

SP-4 ANALYSIS DROID

JN-66 ANALYSIS DROID

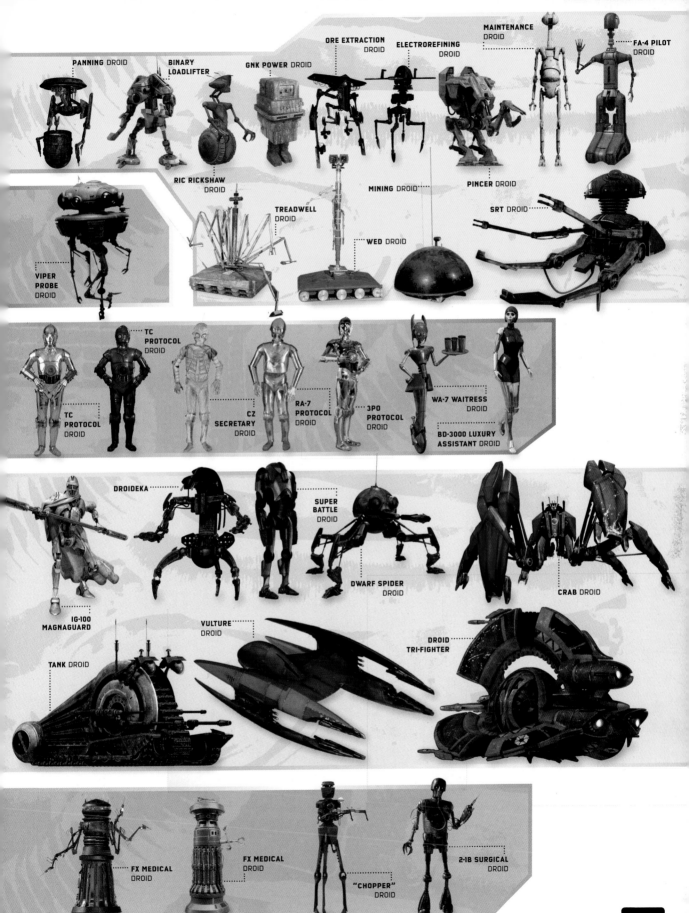

PANNING DROID

BINARY
LOADLIFTER

GNK POWER DROID

ORE EXTRACTION
DROID

ELECTROREFINING
DROID

MAINTENANCE
DROID

FA-4 PILOT
DROID

RIC RICKSHAW
DROID

TREADWELL
DROID

MINING DROID

PINCER DROID

WED DROID

SRT DROID

VIPER
PROBE
DROID

TC PROTOCOL
DROID

TC
PROTOCOL
DROID

CZ
SECRETARY
DROID

RA-7
PROTOCOL
DROID

3PO
PROTOCOL
DROID

WA-7 WAITRESS
DROID

BD-3000 LUXURY
ASSISTANT DROID

DROIDEKA

SUPER
BATTLE
DROID

DWARF SPIDER
DROID

CRAB DROID

IG-100
MAGNAGUARD

VULTURE
DROID

DROID
TRI-FIGHTER

TANK DROID

FX MEDICAL
DROID

FX MEDICAL
DROID

"CHOPPER"
DROID

2-1B SURGICAL
DROID

105

Astromech DROIDS

PRIMARY PHOTORECEPTOR
AND RADAR EYE

Astro-droids are a starship pilot's best friend. These useful little droids keep an electronic eye on flight performance, make repairs, target enemies during space battles, and do the complex math required to plan jumps through hyperspace.

R4-P44

JEDI HELPER
A cautious droid, R4-P17 serves as Obi-Wan Kenobi's astromech until buzz droids destroy her during the Battle of Coruscant.

PROCESSOR
STATE INDICATOR

ACOUSTIC
SIGNALLER

R4-P17

REPUBLIC DROID
R4-P44 assists Obi-Wan Kenobi's clone troopers during the Clone Wars. He flies many missions in ARC-170 starfighters, helping the Republic's brave pilots battle the Separatists.

LOOKING GOOD

After R4-P17's destruction, R4-G9 becomes Obi-Wan's astromech. Other astromechs whistle jealously when they see her fancy bronze dome.

LIFE-FORM SCANNER

DANGEROUS DUTY

Before the Clone Wars, R2-D2 serves aboard Queen Amidala's Royal Starship along with many other astro-droids. When the ship is damaged while fleeing Naboo, R2 and his fellow astro-droids, R2-N3 and G8-R3, race to repair it!

R5-D4

MAJOR MALFUNCTION

R5-D4 is an older astromech model whose circuits often malfunction. He is sold by Jawa droid traders to Luke Skywalker's Uncle Owen. But with a pop and a burst of smoke, R5's motivator breaks, so Owen takes R2-D2 instead.

ASTROMECH DROID

MANUFACTURER: INDUSTRIAL AUTOMATON

HEIGHT: VARIES

GENDER: VARIES

FEATURES: HOLOPROJECTOR, COMPUTER INTERFACE ARM, FIRE EXTINGUISHER, LIFE-FORM SCANNER, REPAIRS DATABASE

WHAT HAPPENS WHEN YOUR STARSHIP IS DAMAGED?

AFTER THE TRADE FEDERATION invades Naboo, Queen Amidala tries to flee in her starship. Trade Federation battleships open fire, and one shot knocks out the ship's shield generator, leaving the ship vulnerable to enemy fire. A few more hits will destroy the starship! Astromech droids rush out onto the ship's gleaming hull to perform emergency repairs in space. They better hurry!

BUZZ DROID DEFEAT

Over the planet Coruscant, buzz droids swarm Obi-Wan and Anakin's starfighters, wreaking havoc with saws and grippers. The droids destroy Obi-Wan's astromech and damage his ship, but Anakin and R2-D2 fight off the buzz droids, enabling the Jedi to continue their mission.

DROID DATA

■ Astromechs' barrel-shaped bodies contain a variety of arms tipped with tools. These tools let them do everything from repairing starships to talking with computers.

SPACE RESCUE

R2-D2 and his fellow droids, R2-B1 and G8-R3, race to repair Amidala's ship as laser blasts burst around them. Only R2 survives, and with seconds left, he repairs the shield and saves the Queen!

STARSHIP DOCTOR

An astro-droid's primary function is to keep starships running properly, so that the pilot can concentrate on flying and fighting. R2 assists Anakin Skywalker on his starfighter and then, many years later, helps his son, Luke.

DANGER ON DAGOBAH

R2's circuits are shielded against water damage, so when he falls into the swamps of Dagobah, he is happy to swim along. That is, until he is swallowed and spat out by a hungry dragonsnake!

R2-D2

R2-D2 looks like any other astromech, but he sure doesn't behave like one! Decades without memory wipes have allowed him to develop a unique personality. He might speak in beeps and whistles, but his friends usually have no problem understanding him!

DROID STATS

MANUFACTURER: INDUSTRIAL AUTOMATON

HEIGHT: 0.96 M (3 FT 2 IN)

GENDER: MALE PROGRAMMING

ALLEGIANCE: REPUBLIC/REBEL ALLIANCE

FEATURES: TOOLS, SENSORS, STARSHIP PILOTING AND MAINTENANCE PROGRAMMING, REPAIRS DATABASE

AERIAL ADVENTURES

R2-D2's thrusters allow him to go places his treads can't take him. But they burn lots of fuel and often break down. By the time he meets Luke, his jets have been removed.

RADAR EYE AND PHOTORECEPTOR

ONBOARD LOGIC FUNCTION DISPLAYS

THRUSTERS MADE BY BROOKS PROPULSION DEVICES

ALL-TERRAIN TREADS

POWERBUS CABLES

FAITHFUL FRIEND

When Luke goes missing on Hoth, R2 knows it's too dangerous to venture out across the snowy planet in search of his master. He can only stand watch at the gate, using his sensors to hunt for the faintest sign that Luke is still alive.

CAN A DROID BE TRUSTED TO COMPLETE A MISSION?

DROIDS FOLLOW THEIR masters' orders, but there's a big difference between obeying simple commands and carrying out a secret mission. When Darth Vader's Star Destroyer captures Princess Leia's ship, she orders a little astromech to find Obi-Wan Kenobi. R2-D2 is a loyal droid and does everything he can to complete his mission.

DROID DATA

■ Some masters use a restraining bolt to prevent their droid from leaving a specific area. This allows the master to control it remotely or even shut it down.

SECRET MISSION
Princess Leia loads the Death Star plans into R2's memory and records a message for Obi-Wan Kenobi. R2's mission: find the exiled Jedi and make sure he hears Leia's plea for help.

LUCKY ESCAPE
R2-D2 and C-3PO flee in an escape pod. Imperial officers detect no life-forms aboard, assume the pod short-circuited, and hold their fire.

DETERMINED
To carry out his mission, R2-D2 tricks Luke into removing his restraining bolt. He then crosses Tatooine's dangerous deserts alone at night in search of Obi-Wan, before finally delivering Leia's message.

COMMUNICATION MODULE BEHIND FACEPLATE

TC-4

DIPLOMATIC DUTY
TC-4 serves Yeb Yeb Adem'thorn, a Senator of the Swokes Swokes species. TC-4 is programmed with extensive knowledge of the money-worshipping Swokes Swokes culture.

DANGEROUS TASK
Nute Gunray is too cowardly to meet with the Jedi Qui-Gon Jinn and Obi-Wan Kenobi when they arrive to discuss the illegal blockade of Naboo. He sends poor TC-14 instead, who has no idea her masters plan to destroy the Jedi with poison gas and battle droids.

Protocol
DROIDS

Protocol droids are programmed to assist Senators, ambassadors, and business executives. They translate unfamiliar languages and help their masters offer proper greetings during negotiations with beings from the galaxy's millions of different species.

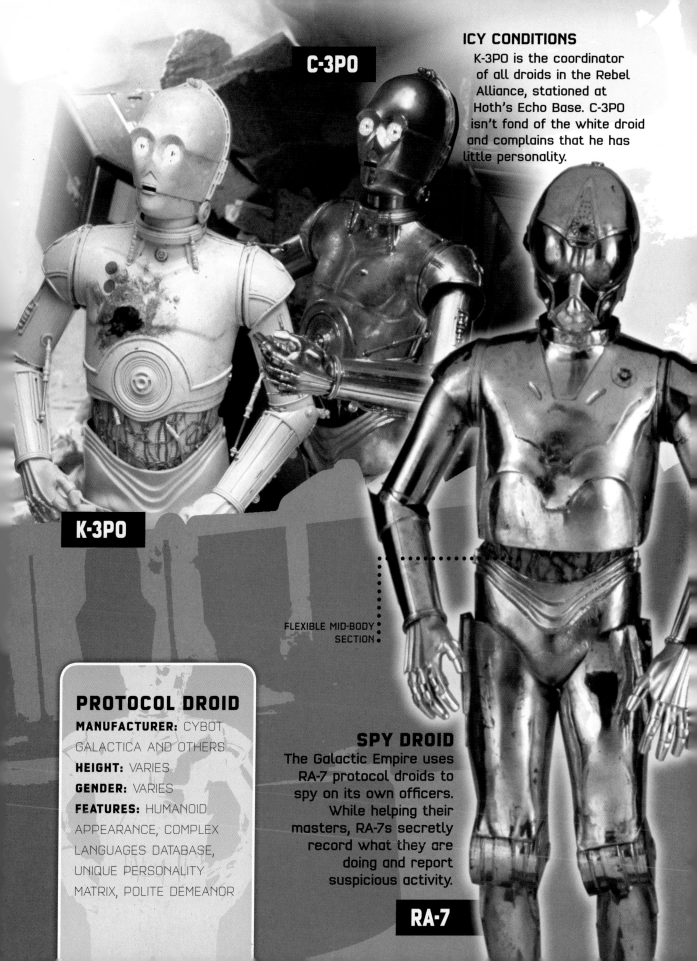

C-3PO

K-3PO

ICY CONDITIONS

K-3PO is the coordinator of all droids in the Rebel Alliance, stationed at Hoth's Echo Base. C-3PO isn't fond of the white droid and complains that he has little personality.

FLEXIBLE MID-BODY SECTION

PROTOCOL DROID

MANUFACTURER: CYBOT GALACTICA AND OTHERS

HEIGHT: VARIES

GENDER: VARIES

FEATURES: HUMANOID APPEARANCE, COMPLEX LANGUAGES DATABASE, UNIQUE PERSONALITY MATRIX, POLITE DEMEANOR

SPY DROID

The Galactic Empire uses RA-7 protocol droids to spy on its own officers. While helping their masters, RA-7s secretly record what they are doing and report suspicious activity.

RA-7

BUILT TO TALK

C-3PO has had many adventures—and hasn't enjoyed any of them. He was programmed to help diplomats and translate alien languages, a job for a civilized droid. So why does he have to travel on those dreadful starships and have people shoot at him?

C-3PO

TOUCH SENSORS

AUDITORY SENSOR

MAIN RECHARGE SOCKET

SHINY BRONZIUM PLATING

Protocol droid C-3PO is fluent in more than six million forms of communication, and programmed to be polite and helpful. He travels with Padmé Amidala on diplomatic missions for the Republic Senate, and later helps Princess Leia as she seeks support for the Rebellion.

THANK THE MAKER
C-3PO doesn't remember this, but he was built by young Anakin Skywalker, using parts from several protocol droids.

GOLDEN GOD
The Ewoks think C-3PO is a god, thanks to his shiny, golden casings. He uses his ability to speak the language of the Ewoks to convince the tribe to join the Rebellion.

WE'RE DOOMED!
C-3PO expects the worst in any situation, but he becomes annoyed when his friends say he worries too much. Why can't everybody understand how dangerous the galaxy is?

C-3PO
MANUFACTURER: CUSTOM-BUILT
HEIGHT: 1.73 M (5 FT 8 IN)
GENDER: MALE PROGRAMMING
ALLEGIANCE: REPUBLIC/REBEL ALLIANCE
FEATURES: DIPLOMATIC PROGRAMMING, KNOWLEDGE OF CULTURES AND LANGUAGES

C-3PO hasn't always looked the same. Over the years, he's been on many adventures and served lots of different masters. His outer casings have changed several times, and tell a fascinating story.

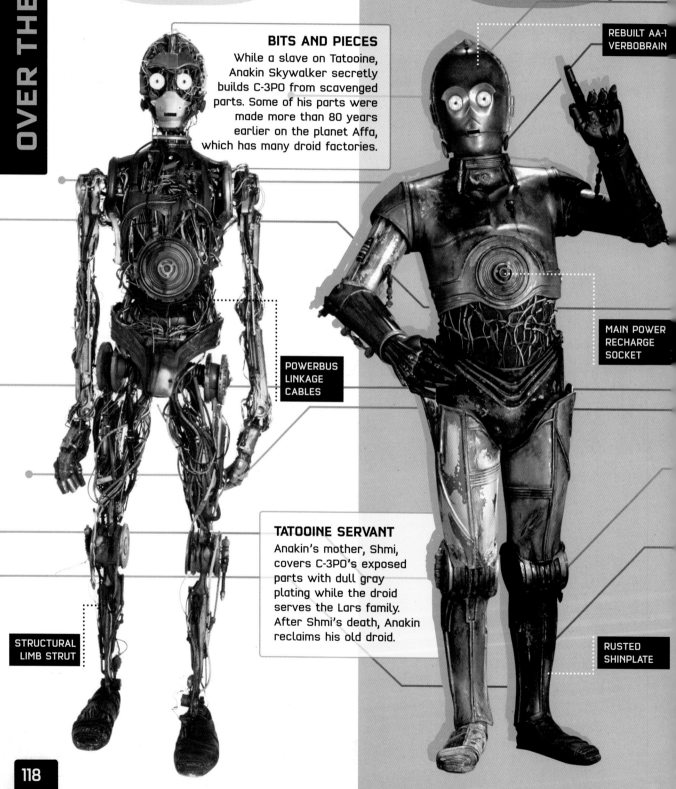

BITS AND PIECES
While a slave on Tatooine, Anakin Skywalker secretly builds C-3PO from scavenged parts. Some of his parts were made more than 80 years earlier on the planet Affa, which has many droid factories.

POWERBUS LINKAGE CABLES

STRUCTURAL LIMB STRUT

TATOOINE SERVANT
Anakin's mother, Shmi, covers C-3PO's exposed parts with dull gray plating while the droid serves the Lars family. After Shmi's death, Anakin reclaims his old droid.

REBUILT AA-1 VERBOBRAIN

MAIN POWER RECHARGE SOCKET

RUSTED SHINPLATE

118

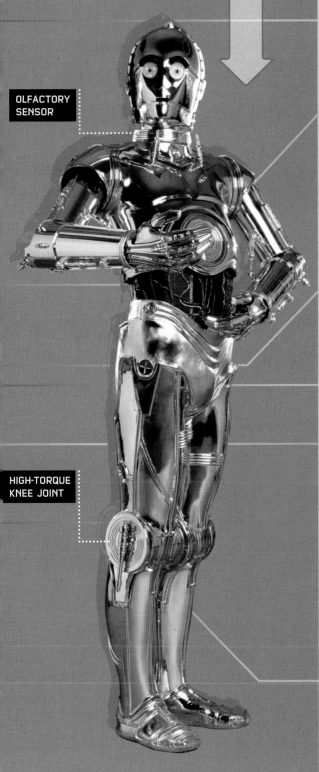

SENATOR'S SERVANT

Anakin gives C-3PO to Padmé Amidala as a wedding present. As a Senator's translator, C-3PO has to fit in at important meetings and fancy diplomatic parties, so Padmé refits him with gleaming golden plating.

OLFACTORY SENSOR

HIGH-TORQUE KNEE JOINT

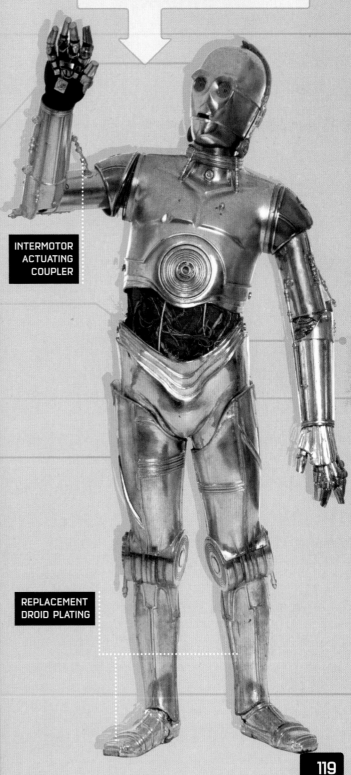

WEAR AND TEAR

After the fall of the Republic, C-3PO's memory is erased. He now works for the Rebel Alliance and has a number of replacement parts, which were added whenever part of his casings needed repair.

INTERMOTOR ACTUATING COUPLER

REPLACEMENT DROID PLATING

QUEEN AMIDALA
R2-D2 serves the Naboo Royal House. One day, he saves Queen Padmé Amidala's life and permanently joins her staff.

R2-D2

This small astromech serves two royal houses, a moisture farmer, a Hutt crimelord, and two Jedi. He learns some of the galaxy's biggest secrets over the years, but he keeps them to himself.

BAIL ORGANA
After Padmé's death and Anakin's fall to the dark side, R2-D2 and C-3PO spend years serving Alderaan's ruling Organa family.

ANAKIN SKYWALKER
Padmé gives R2-D2 to Anakin as a wedding gift, trusting the little droid to keep her husband safe in his Jedi starfighter.

ANAKIN SKYWALKER
When Anakin returns to Tatooine, he reclaims the droid he built as a young slave.

PADMÉ AMIDALA
Anakin gives C-3PO to Padmé as a wedding gift, hoping the droid can help with her duties as a Senator.

SHMI SKYWALKER
When Shmi marries Cliegg Lars, she takes C-3PO to serve on the Lars moisture farm.

ANAKIN SKYWALKER
Young slave Anakin secretly builds C-3PO to help his mother Shmi around their hovel.

TWO DROIDS:
MANY OWNERS

R2-D2 and C-3PO first met long ago, when they had different masters and lived on different planets. During the Clone Wars, the two droids were brought together again, eventually becoming a pair always owned by the same master.

JAWAS
Escaping capture on the *Tantive IV*, the droids wander the wastes of Tatooine, where a band of Jawas grab them.

LUKE SKYWALKER
After Owen is killed by Imperial troops, his stepson, Luke, becomes the droids' master.

PRINCESS LEIA
The droids accompany Bail's stepdaughter Leia—secretly, Padmé's daughter—on missions aboard her starship, the *Tantive IV*.

OWEN LARS
Moisture farmer Owen Lars buys the droids from the Jawas, not recognizing C-3PO, his family's old droid, with his gold plating.

JABBA THE HUTT
As part of a plan to save Han Solo, Luke gives the droids to the gangster Jabba the Hutt, who puts them to work as servants.

LUKE SKYWALKER
Rescued from Jabba, the droids continue to serve Luke and his friends on many more adventures.

C-3PO

Constructed from salvaged parts, C-3PO has been owned by lots of very important people. A memory wipe, ordered by Bail Organa, leaves C-3PO unaware that he has witnessed crucial events in galactic history.

HOW DO R2-D2 AND C-3PO HELP EACH OTHER?

R2-D2 AND C-3PO ARE TWO very different droids: R2 was designed to help pilots and engineers with their starships, while C-3PO helps diplomats and politicians do their jobs. But the two friends often find themselves thrown together in tricky situations. Luckily, their unique skills complement each other and they work together to get each other out of trouble.

DROID DATA

■ R2-D2 can speak only in standard droid language Binary—also known as Droidspeak. Yet, thanks to his high-level programming, R2 can understand a variety of other languages.

PICKING UP THE PIECES
C-3PO isn't a combat droid, and is terrified to find his head has been separated from his body—and welded onto a battle droid! Fortunately, R2 is able to put C-3PO's metal body back together, ignoring C-3PO's anxious complaints as he works.

R2 TO THE RESCUE!

R2-D2's wide assortment of tools means he can fix just about anything. When C-3PO is blasted apart on Cloud City, R2 happily fixes his friend. He just takes a short break to repair the *Millennium Falcon*'s hyperdrive, helping everyone on board escape from Darth Vader.

TRUE FRIENDSHIP

Few living beings can understand R2-D2's language of beeps and whistles, but C-3PO finds his friend's electronic noises easy to interpret. C-3PO often translates what R2 has to say, although he politely leaves out any comments that might be a bit too rude.

WATCH OUT FOR THE PIT DROIDS!

Pit droids are a common sight in Podracing arenas. The little droids are strong and never question orders—but they can also be a bit foolish. They like to have fun while doing their jobs, but they are often reckless, which sometimes leads to unfortunate accidents.

AIR TROUBLES

The thrusters on Ebe E. Endocott's Podracer need to be unblocked. While two pit droids argue about who will get on whose shoulders to do it, one activates a third's air gun, blasting a fourth with a burst of compressed air.

SOMETHING BORROWED

Ebe's air gun is out of power, so his droids borrow one from Ody Mandrell's crew. Ody's droids weren't using it, were they?

FULL OF BAD IDEAS

Pit droids are tough enough to survive almost any accident, so they never worry about getting damaged. But mechanics sometimes wish they did worry! The simple-minded droids have been known to think up some very foolish ideas, like trying to peer inside an engine while it's still running!

WATCH YOUR STEP!

The thrusters need new baffles. A pit droid grabs an armload and rushes off—but he doesn't see the deactivated pit droid lying in his path...

HARD AT WORK?

Pit droids are strong enough to carry an afterburner, no problem. However, they don't need it to fix Ebe's Podracer, they just want to stand on top of it so they can reach the thrusters!

JOINTS ARE
VULNERABLE
POINTS

LIMBS FOLD FOR
TRANSPORT

SECURITY DROID

ROGER ROGER

Battle droid commanders are marked
by yellow spots on their heads and
chests. They order regular droids
into battle using military strategies
downloaded into their brain databases.

ON GUARD

Security droids have
red markings, but are
functionally the same
as regular battle droids.
They are often assigned
to patrol duties aboard
Separatist warships.

Battle
DROIDS

Battle droids aren't smart, but they
don't need to be! They are simple war
robots programmed to follow orders
and overwhelm enemies by attacking in
huge numbers. Go ahead and blast them,
the Separatists will just build more!

BATTLE DROID

MANUFACTURER: BAKTOID
HEIGHT: 1.91 M (6 FT 3 IN)
GENDER: MALE PROGRAMMING
FEATURES: E-5 BLASTER RIFLE, SOME UNITS HAVE TOUGHER ARMOR AND SPECIALIZED PROGRAMMING

SIGNAL ANTENNA

SIMPLE VOCODER

BATTLE DROID

BATTLE OF NABOO

Evil Darth Sidious manipulates the Trade Federation into invading Naboo. Thousands of battle droids quickly occupy the green planet's cities and capture the Royal Palace.

E-5 BLASTER

TRIGGER HAPPY

Known as "clankers," battle droids become confused when they find themselves in situations for which they haven't been programmed. But beware: they often solve problems by firing their blasters.

DANGEROUS GOODS

The Trade Federation's enormous Droid Control Ships direct the movements of battleships, which are filled with assault vehicles, droid starfighters, and battle droids.

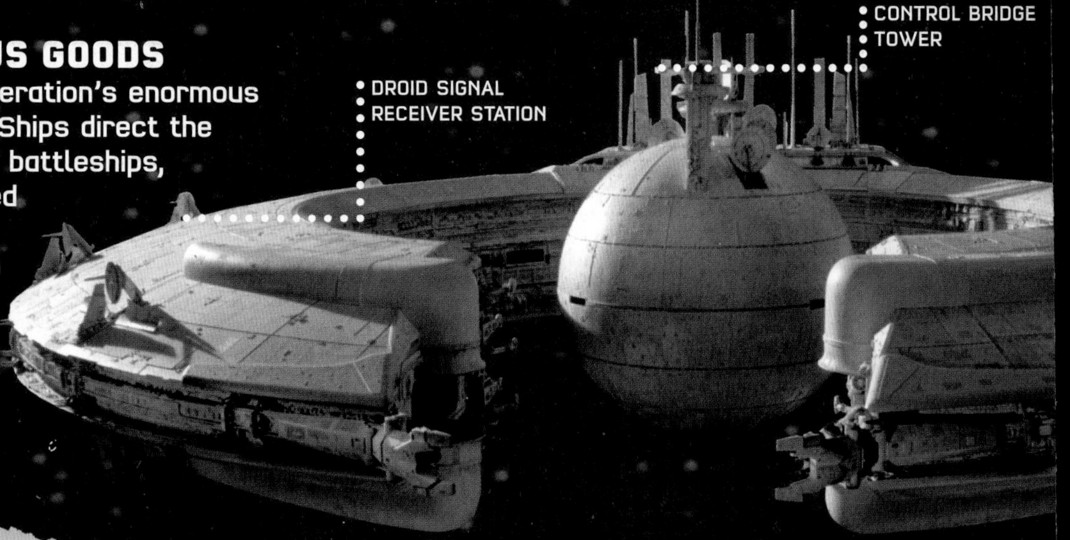

DROID SIGNAL RECEIVER STATION

CONTROL BRIDGE TOWER

UNINVITED GUESTS

During the invasion of Naboo, landing craft descend to the planet's surface and unload battle tanks and MTTs (multi-troop transports).

FOLDED BATTLE DROIDS

DROID PAYLOAD

Lots of heavily armored MTT carriers rumble from the landing sites to the battlefield. Each MTT opens its hatches to reveal storage racks holding 112 battle droids.

REPULSOR COOLING FINS

Preparing for BATTLE

When the Trade Federation decides to invade Naboo, it uses its experience transporting goods in freighters to move battle droids quickly into position and prepare them for war.

READY TO RUMBLE

The racks unload battle droids, still folded to save space. A signal from the Droid Control Ship tells the droids to unfold and prepare for battle, a process that takes less than 15 seconds.

- DROID DEPLOYED ON BATTLEFIELD, STILL FOLDED IN TRANSPORT MODE

- ARMS AND LEGS UNFURL AND DROID CHECKS GYROSCOPIC SYSTEMS

- IN STANDING POSITION, DROID PERFORMS MORE SYSTEM CHECKS

- HEAD LOCKS IN PLACE AND DROID SENDS READY SIGNAL TO DROID CONTROL SHIP

- DROID DRAWS BLASTER AND AWAITS ORDERS

WHY IS IT POINTLESS TO **PLEAD MERCY** WITH A BATTLE DROID?

BATTLE DROIDS ARE dangerous. Not only are they designed to destroy, but they also cannot think for themselves or question orders. Fortunately for clever Jedi and well-trained clone troopers, the slow-witted and physically weak droids are fairly easy to obliterate.

ONE MIND
Battle droids are programmed to have no emotions, so appealing to their sense of compassion is futile. Also, as identical robots, they all think the same—so asking for a second opinion will get you nowhere!

DOES NOT COMPUTE
Logic and reason mean nothing to battle droids. They lack the brain capacity to process any information that falls outside their narrow programming, so there's no point trying to have a discussion with them. When Obi-Wan tells the droids that he needs the ship they are guarding, their reaction to the unfamiliar information is to attack.

RELENTLESS
Once battle droids receive their orders, they will not stop until their mission is complete—or if they are destroyed.

HOW CAN YOU DEFEAT
BATTLE DROIDS?

THE TRADE FEDERATION'S battle droids are not the greatest individual soldiers, but their strength lies in numbers. The Gungans of Naboo fight bravely and are able to destroy individual battle droids quite easily, but they are vastly outnumbered. To truly defeat the Droid Army, the signal that controls the droids must be shut down.

DROID DATA

■ After the Battle of Naboo, the Separatists reprogram some battle droids so they can move and fight without orders from a central computer.

LIGHTSABER POWER

Jedi like Qui-Gon Jinn make short work of battle droids with their lightsabers. But even a Jedi can't win when faced with thousands of these metal troopers.

DESTROY CENTRAL COMMAND

Naboo pilots fly into space and launch an attack on the orbiting Droid Control Ship. When young Anakin Skywalker blows up the ship, the computer controlling the battle droids is destroyed, too. In a second, the Trade Federation's terrifying army has been turned into silent scrap metal!

ONE LITTLE SHOVE

Without the signal from the Droid Control Ship, the battle droids shut down. All it takes is one little shove, and they fall to the ground. The delighted Gungans cheer as they push them over!

Super
BATTLE DROIDS

B2 Battle Droids—known as super battle droids—are the deadly frontliners of the Separatists' Droid Army. They are big, tough, and dumb. Super battle droids often march ahead of other Separatist droids, smashing through enemy troops and anything else that gets in their way.

BIG MISTAKE!
Super battle droids think smaller droids are weak and useless. This turns out to be a big mistake when two of them underestimate R2-D2, who squirts them with oil and sets them on fire using his thrusters. That'll teach them a lesson!

RAPID-FIRE DUAL LASER CANNON

COGNITIVE MODULE

MUSCLE MACHINE
The Separatists designed B2s to make up for the weaknesses of regular battle droids. B2s have stronger armor, more powerful blasters, and do not rely on a droid control signal.

FLEXIBLE ARMORED MIDSECTION

SUPER BATTLE DROID

MANUFACTURER: BAKTOID

HEIGHT: 1.93 M (6 FT 4 IN)

GENDER: MALE PROGRAMMING

FEATURES: SENSORS, COMMUNICATIONS GEAR, BUILT-IN BLASTERS

How Are DROIDS MADE?

Giant factories on the planet Geonosis produce new armies of battle droids for the Trade Federation. In the heat and noise of the factory, droids and Geonosian drones supervise assembly lines that never stop creating machines.

1 RAW MATERIALS

The Geonosians mine rock from the ring that surrounds their planet. Huge machines crush the rock, superlasers melt it, impurities are burned off, and the molten ore is poured from huge vats into molds, cooling to form droid parts.

HIVE WORKERS

Geonosians are insect-like beings who live in hives. Most Geonosian factory workers are drones that never question orders and barely think for themselves.

DROID DATA

■ Geonosis's droid factory is actually quite small compared to the giant plants on ancient droid-making planets such as Affa, Mechis, Telti, and Cyrillia.

2 SUPERVISION

Geonosian workers and specialized droids keep a careful eye on the factory's assembly lines, looking for problems that could stop production. A SRT droid, which is normally used for transporting materials, will spot an unfamiliar droid and remove him from the conveyor belt.

> "**Machines** making machines. How perverse."
> — C-3PO

3 CONVEYORS

Droid parts are stamped and finished and then speed around the factory on conveyor belts. As the parts go by, machines fuse them together and add more sophisticated systems.

4 KEEP MOVING!

Restarting the Geonosis factory's conveyors takes a long time, so the production line stops only if a big problem occurs. Small difficulties such as an incorrect head aren't worth halting the machines!

5 QUALITY CONTROL

Normally, a factory supervisor checks all completed droids and rejects any mistakes. But Geonosis is under attack, so even though a mix-up leaves C-3PO and a battle droid with switched heads and bodies, the batch is sent straight into combat!

DROIDEKA

MANUFACTURER: COLICOIDS
HEIGHT: 1.83 M (6 FT)
GENDER: NONE
FEATURES: ENERGY SHIELDS, RADIATION SENSORS

TROUBLE ON WHEELS

Droidekas travel by rolling; curling their arms, heads, and legs into a wheel. They then move with frightening speed to attack their enemies.

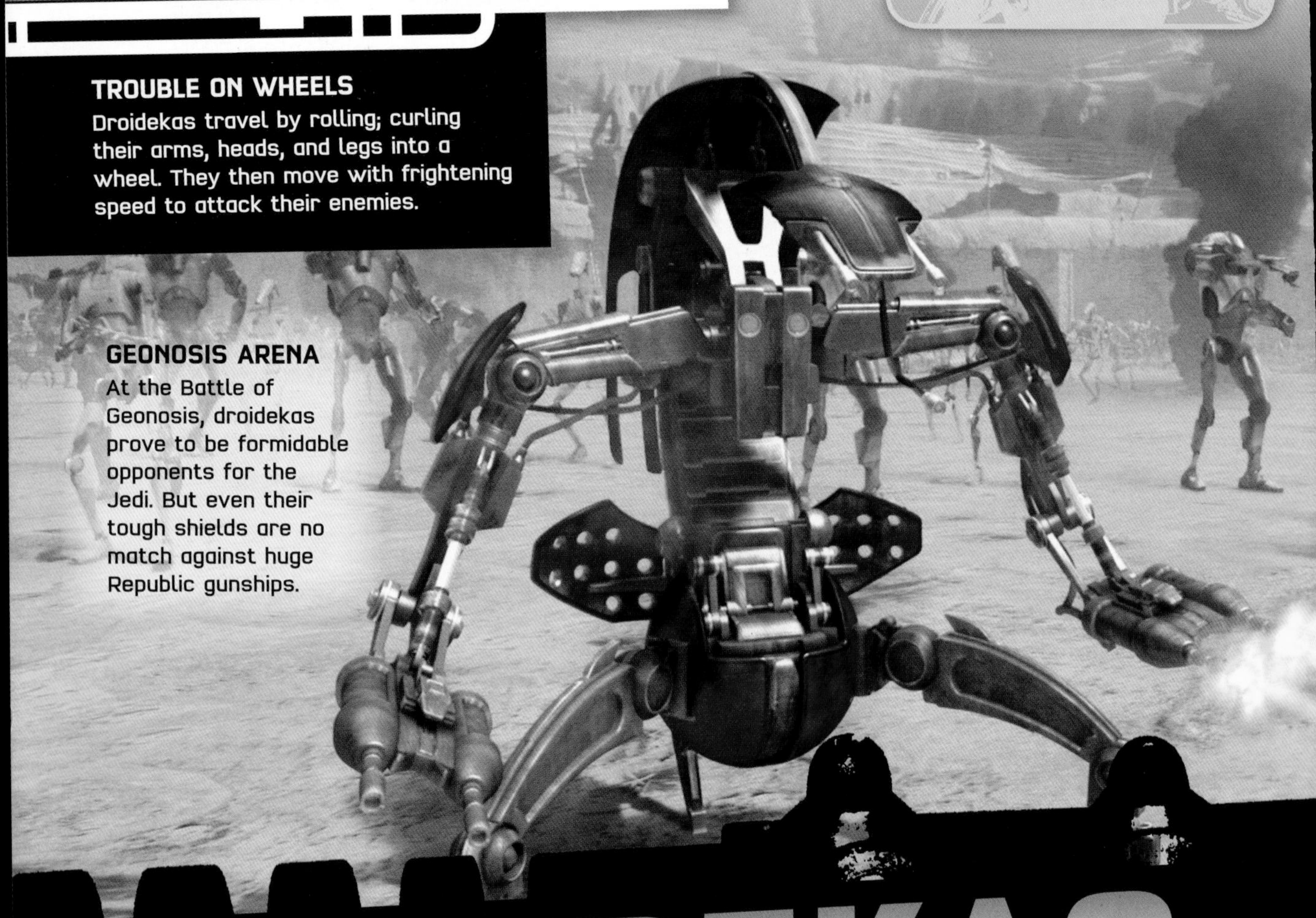

GEONOSIS ARENA

At the Battle of Geonosis, droidekas prove to be formidable opponents for the Jedi. But even their tough shields are no match against huge Republic gunships.

DROIDEKAS

Officially known as destroyer droids, these three-legged droids are some of the strongest units in the Separatist army. Clone troopers fear their powerful, rapid-fire cannons and impenetrable energy shields, and even Jedi Knights treat droidekas with respect.

PRIMARY SENSOR ANTENNA

RAPID-FIRE LASER CANNON

SHIELD PROJECTOR PLATE

SPECIAL DELIVERY
The vicious insect species known as the Colicoids created the early droideka models. As payment, they asked for 50 space barges full of exotic meat. Deal!

REACTOR HOUSING

139

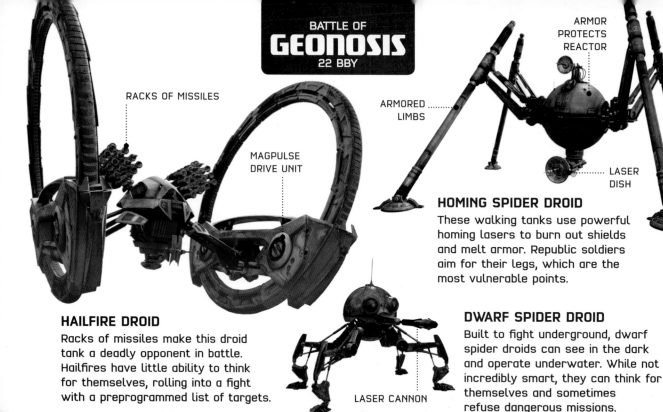

RACKS OF MISSILES

MAGPULSE
DRIVE UNIT

ARMOR
PROTECTS
REACTOR

ARMORED
LIMBS

LASER
DISH

HOMING SPIDER DROID
These walking tanks use powerful homing lasers to burn out shields and melt armor. Republic soldiers aim for their legs, which are the most vulnerable points.

HAILFIRE DROID
Racks of missiles make this droid tank a deadly opponent in battle. Hailfires have little ability to think for themselves, rolling into a fight with a preprogrammed list of targets.

LASER CANNON

DWARF SPIDER DROID
Built to fight underground, dwarf spider droids can see in the dark and operate underwater. While not incredibly smart, they can think for themselves and sometimes refuse dangerous missions.

BATTLEFIELD DROIDS

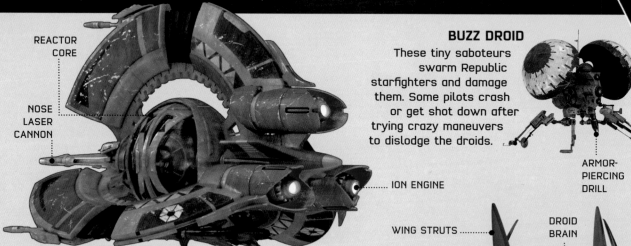

REACTOR
CORE

NOSE
LASER
CANNON

BUZZ DROID
These tiny saboteurs swarm Republic starfighters and damage them. Some pilots crash or get shot down after trying crazy maneuvers to dislodge the droids.

ION ENGINE

ARMOR-
PIERCING
DRILL

WING STRUTS

DROID
BRAIN

TRI-FIGHTER
Introduced late in the Clone Wars, these droid starfighters are heavily armed, fast, and highly maneuverable. They fight with blaster cannons, missiles, and projectiles that contain buzz droids.

DISCORD MISSILE
CONTAINS BUZZ
DROIDS

VULTURE DROID
Vultures aren't nearly as effective as tri-fighters during space battles, but are cheaper to build and easier to repair. They can fight on the ground by walking on their wings.

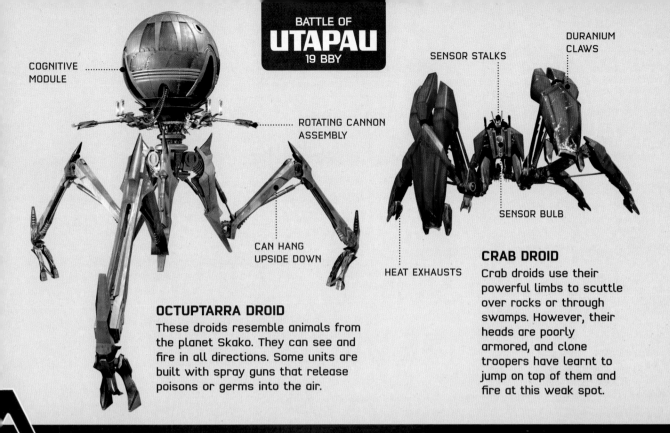

COGNITIVE MODULE

SENSOR STALKS

DURANIUM CLAWS

ROTATING CANNON ASSEMBLY

SENSOR BULB

CAN HANG UPSIDE DOWN

HEAT EXHAUSTS

OCTUPTARRA DROID

These droids resemble animals from the planet Skako. They can see and fire in all directions. Some units are built with spray guns that release poisons or germs into the air.

CRAB DROID

Crab droids use their powerful limbs to scuttle over rocks or through swamps. However, their heads are poorly armored, and clone troopers have learnt to jump on top of them and fire at this weak spot.

The Separatists are afraid of getting injured, so they stay as far from the battlefield as possible, relying on droids to do their fighting for them. Many Separatist war machines are giant robots designed to fight independently on land and in space.

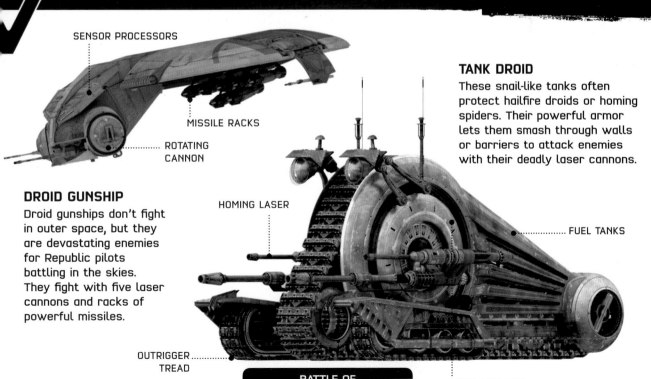

SENSOR PROCESSORS

MISSILE RACKS

ROTATING CANNON

TANK DROID

These snail-like tanks often protect hailfire droids or homing spiders. Their powerful armor lets them smash through walls or barriers to attack enemies with their deadly laser cannons.

DROID GUNSHIP

Droid gunships don't fight in outer space, but they are devastating enemies for Republic pilots battling in the skies. They fight with five laser cannons and racks of powerful missiles.

HOMING LASER

FUEL TANKS

OUTRIGGER TREAD

DRIVE AXIS HUB

141

WHY IS THE SEPARATIST ARMY SO POWERFUL?

THE SEPARATISTS HAVE several advantages in their war against the Republic: Firstly, they can overwhelm planets with huge numbers of battle droids. Secondly, they have lots of money to run enormous factories, which build new types of droids for different situations. Finally, the Separatist leaders can rest assured their droid troops will carry out orders without asking questions.

OUT OF HARM'S WAY
Separatist commanders transmit orders from large Droid Control Ships. Even if the battle droids on the ground are attacked, the command center remains safe in outer space, ready to regroup or deploy more droid soldiers.

DIVERSE DROIDS

The Separatists use many different kinds
of droids, with models designed for battle
on land, in the air, or under the sea. Tank
droids, crab droids, and spider droids can
even fight both on land and under water!

LAUNCH MISSILES!
Vulture droids and droid tri-fighters are armed with discord missiles, which pack seven buzz droids into an armored shell. Discord missiles are extremely fast and maneuverable, able to keep up with even the best Jedi star pilots.

BUZZ DROID
DEPLOYMENT

The deadly Colicoid species got the idea for buzz droids after seeing teams of tiny repair droids scuttle across freighters' hulls fixing problems. Buzz droids are programmed to create problems instead. Launched from speedy missiles, they swarm Republic starships, using mechanical limbs ending in drills, cutting torches, and saws to rip through metal hulls and systems, turning ships into flying scrap.

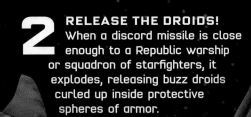

2 RELEASE THE DROIDS!

When a discord missile is close enough to a Republic warship or squadron of starfighters, it explodes, releasing buzz droids curled up inside protective spheres of armor.

3 TARGET ACQUIRED!

The buzz droids have simple sensors and small rocket jets for maneuvering. Once in space, they lock on to the nearest signal in hopes of finding a Republic ship to tear apart.

4 TIME TO OPERATE!

After locating a target, a buzz droid extends its legs and pops out of its shell, latching onto a ship with its magnetic feet. It scuttles along the hull until it reaches a weak point. Then it extends its pincers and arms and goes to work.

5 MISSION ACCOMPLISHED!

Buzz droids' memory banks are loaded with information about enemy ships, telling them where to strike. The droids work in swarms, tearing apart the ship's systems until their target has been reduced to a useless hulk of scrap metal, doomed to float forever in the emptiness of space.

WHY ARE VULTURE DROIDS SO DANGEROUS?

VULTURE DROIDS ARE frightening foes, both in space and on the ground. In space, these speedy droid starfighters swarm Republic ships like clouds of biting insects, overwhelming their defenses. On land, they can also transform into walking mode, using the tips of their wings like feet. In this configuration they guard warships and can even defend Separatist ground units.

HIGH SPEED
Vulture droids rely on simple strategies for space combat. They aren't as smart as living pilots, but their mechanical reflexes are much faster, and droid brains help them work together to fight enemy ships.

READY FOR LAUNCH
While in walk mode, Vulture droids patrol the hulls of Separatist warships instead of waiting in hangars. If enemy starfighters get too close, the droids only need a few seconds to switch to flight mode and launch.

A Day in the Life of a DROID TRADER

Droid traders are always on the lookout for a bargain—or a foolish customer! Watto prides himself on having a keen eye for machines, the right touch with tools, and a shop overflowing with parts.

1 CLEAN UP JUNKSHOP

Watto's shop looks crowded and chaotic, but the Toydarian trader knows exactly where everything is. He'd be very angry if his young slave, Anakin Skywalker, messed it up!

DROID DATA

■ Watto was a soldier on the planet Toydaria before moving to Tatooine. He lived with a group of Jawas, learning their droid trading ways, before he set up his own junkshop.

2 FIND DROIDS TO SELL

Broken, abandoned droids are often found in Tatooine's towns or sold in pieces at a market stall. One look is enough to tell a smart trader whether a droid can be repaired or if it is just junk.

"No money, no parts, no deal!"
Watto

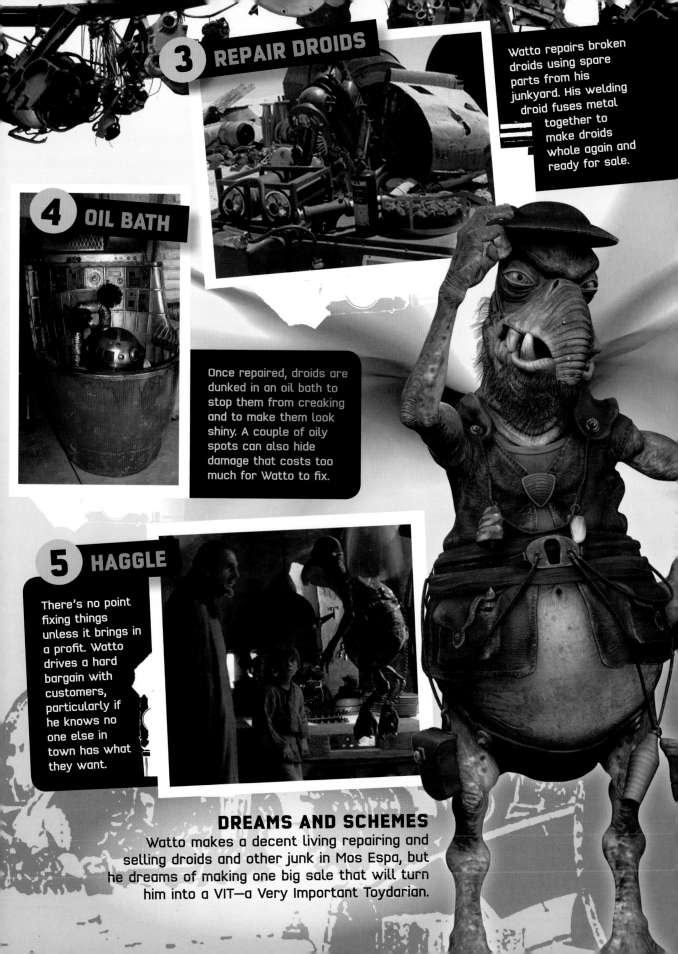

3 REPAIR DROIDS

Watto repairs broken droids using spare parts from his junkyard. His welding droid fuses metal together to make droids whole again and ready for sale.

4 OIL BATH

Once repaired, droids are dunked in an oil bath to stop them from creaking and to make them look shiny. A couple of oily spots can also hide damage that costs too much for Watto to fix.

5 HAGGLE

There's no point fixing things unless it brings in a profit. Watto drives a hard bargain with customers, particularly if he knows no one else in town has what they want.

DREAMS AND SCHEMES

Watto makes a decent living repairing and selling droids and other junk in Mos Espa, but he dreams of making one big sale that will turn him into a VIT—a Very Important Toydarian.

DROIDS FOR SALE

For every job, there's a perfect droid. Do you need a factory supervisor? A camera to record your Podrace? A cargo loader for all your heavy lifting? Look no further—a trusty mechanical helper is all you need!

HOVER LOADER
If you need to transfer cargo between ships and freighters, this strong, simple-minded droid won't let you down.

PK WORKER DROID
This durable droid can be programmed to perform the same tasks over and over again—no matter how dull!

BINARY LOADLIFTER
Programmed for heavy lifting and not much thinking, the binary loadlifter will make light of all your heavy loads.

CAM DROID
Record important events with your very own camera droid! It can transmit crystal-clear footage to multiple viewscreens.

GNK POWER DROID
Never be without power again! This battery droid can supply energy to ships, machines, and other droids.

MAINTENANCE DROID
The Otoga-222 can perform a diverse variety of labor tasks. Designed to display curiosity, this droid is always learning.

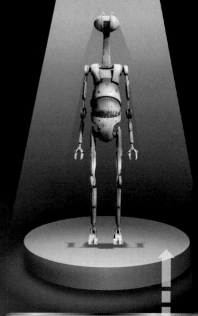

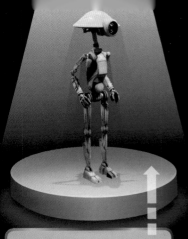

PIT DROID
Fixing a Podracer is child's play for a pit droid! This strong droid is hard-working—and cheap!

SRT DROID
A welcome addition to any factory, the SRT droid moves bulk materials and supervises assembly lines.

ANALYSIS DROID
For all your data analysis needs, this droid boasts sensors and access to computer databases.

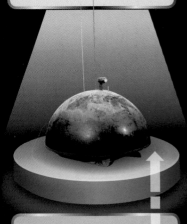

DEMOLITION DROID
Essential for any building site, this blast-proof droid sets and detonates explosives safely.

GATEKEEPER DROID
Keep unwanted visitors out with this popular droid. Equipped with a camera eye and voice box.

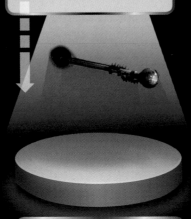

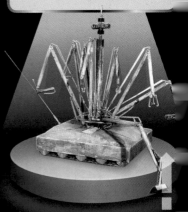

TREADWELL DROID
For the simplest repair jobs, look no further than the treadwell. Skilled and sturdy, it won't disappoint.

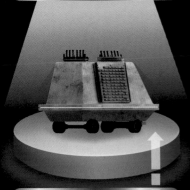

MOUSE DROID
This tiny droid will deliver your messages without fail. It can also stand guard or escort visitors.

ROLO-DROID
Need to keep an eye on your slaves? This modified PK droid will guard all your property with care.

EXPLORER DROID
Looking to explore alien worlds? This floating droid gathers and transmits a wide range of data.

How to Choose
A DROID

Buying a used droid could save you money, but beware! Dishonest traders often sell damaged droids or machines with faulty programming. Make sure you choose your droid carefully.

1. SEE EVERYTHING FIRST

Before you start haggling, make sure you check out everything that's for sale, and never let a trader know what you're interested in. If you're too eager, a trader may hide a cheaper model at the back of the sandcrawler, so you are forced to pay more.

TREADWELL REPAIR DROID

2. ASK ABOUT ORIGINS

Ask where a droid came from, and see if you believe the trader's story. Or, if the droid can talk, ask it yourself. But remember, droids are sometimes programmed to lie. Is that protocol droid with the gold casing really an expert in programming binary loadlifters?

R2-D2

3. TAKE A CLOSE LOOK

DROID DATA

A droid that looks fine on the outside can be a mess inside, so look out for frozen gears, loose wires, carbon-scoring, or a bad motivator. If a trader won't let you examine a droid closely, what is he trying to hide?

4. RETURN IF FAULTY

Ask for a guarantee that you can return the droid if something goes wrong. If there's a problem, don't delay—it's hard to get a refund or trade in a bad droid once the sandcrawler has rolled on to the next moisture farm.

"Uncle Owen! This Artoo unit has a bad motivator!"

Luke Skywalker

R5-D4

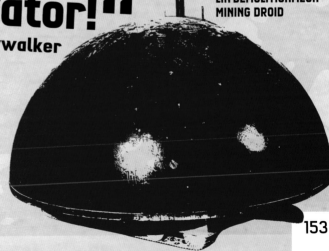

LIN DEMOLITIONMECH MINING DROID

WHY IS IT A
HARD LIFE
BEING A DROID?

VERY FEW OF the droids in the galaxy enjoy the freedom that most life-forms take for granted. Many droids are treated like slaves by their owners, then cast aside when they are no longer needed. The most a droid can hope for is that it will be bought by kind masters who will take good care of it.

ATTACKED IN BATTLE
War destroys millions of droids, whether they're combat droids built to fight in place of living beings, or astromechs caught in the middle of space battles. In the Battle of Coruscant, buzz droids tear off the head of poor R4-P17, Obi-Wan Kenobi's astromech.

OWNED BY OTHERS

Even kind masters can treat droids as property: C-3PO is shocked when Luke gives him and R2-D2 to Jabba the Hutt. He doesn't know that it's part of Luke's plan to rescue Han Solo.

CONSTANT DANGER

Some living beings like to torment defenseless droids, but sometimes droids are also cruel, or they do terrible things because of glitches in their programming. Beneath Jabba's palace is a grim dungeon where droids enjoy making other droids suffer. 8D8 is employed to terrify other droids. He uses heated metal to make a GNK power droid shriek with fear!

155

Service DROIDS

Service droids are designed to help living beings with small but necessary tasks. They must be able to communicate clearly and politely, and to follow instructions immediately.

FOR-HIRE HAULER

Despite their name, rickshaw droids are actually general-purpose labor droids used for many tasks, not just pulling carriages. Travelers should watch out for droids who are programmed to increase fares by taking roundabout routes.

RIC RICKSHAW DROID

POWERFUL GRIPPERS

SPACEPORT SERVANT

FA-5 droids are a common sight in spaceports, where they carry luggage and arrange transportation for travelers. They often bear the insignia of shuttle companies. Some FA-5s also work in private homes as butlers or servants.

WHISTLE FUNCTION FOR HAILING TRANSPORTATION

BALANCE GYRO FOR DRIVE WHEEL

FA-5 VALET DROID

INDICATOR LIGHT SHOWS IF DROID IS FOR HIRE

RAIN OR SHINE

Rickshaw droids often pull a covered carriage with seats for two. Travelers are relieved to find shelter from the sun or rain, while the droid rolls on, unaffected by the weather.

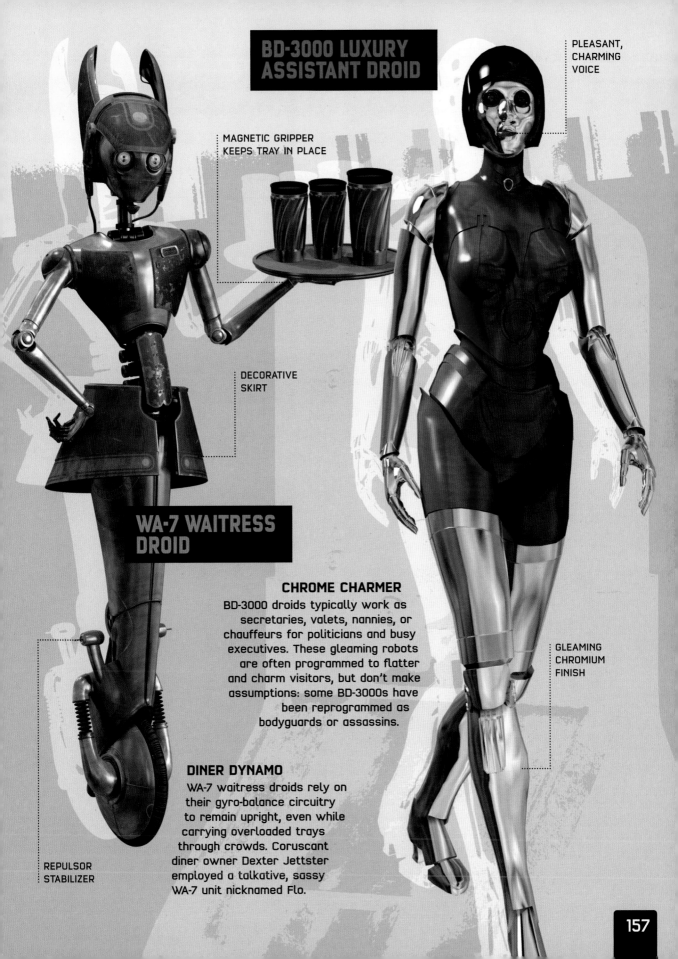

BD-3000 LUXURY ASSISTANT DROID

MAGNETIC GRIPPER
KEEPS TRAY IN PLACE

PLEASANT,
CHARMING
VOICE

DECORATIVE
SKIRT

WA-7 WAITRESS DROID

CHROME CHARMER

BD-3000 droids typically work as secretaries, valets, nannies, or chauffeurs for politicians and busy executives. These gleaming robots are often programmed to flatter and charm visitors, but don't make assumptions: some BD-3000s have been reprogrammed as bodyguards or assassins.

GLEAMING
CHROMIUM
FINISH

DINER DYNAMO

WA-7 waitress droids rely on their gyro-balance circuitry to remain upright, even while carrying overloaded trays through crowds. Coruscant diner owner Dexter Jettster employed a talkative, sassy WA-7 unit nicknamed Flo.

REPULSOR
STABILIZER

DROID VISION: TECHNICAL

Not all droids see in the same way. What they see, and how well they see it, depends on what they are programmed to do. The visual capabilities of technical droids vary widely, from extremely basic, to multi-functional.

ENERGY DISTRIBUTION MODE

POWER LEVEL INDICATOR

POWER SOURCE DETECTION

DIRECTIONAL INDICATOR

OBSTACLE AVOIDANCE GRID

RECHARGE STATUS

GNK
POWER DROID

Power droids are walking batteries designed to recharge other droids, vehicles, and machines. A power droid walking around Mos Eisley sees the world in terms of power levels and energy sources.

R2-D2 is programmed to navigate starships through outer space, even during ferocious space battles. To do this, his visual sensors must have many functions. He can be linked up to computer databases detailing star charts and vehicle data.

A PILOT'S BEST FRIEND

R2-D2's holographic camera is designed to display 3-D representations of space battles so the pilot can identify enemies and plot his course. The technology can also be used to record secret messages.

PROCESSOR STATE INDICATOR

3-D HOLOGRAPHIC SENSOR DATA

SENSOR SCAN DIRECTION

RANGE INDICATORS

COMMAND DIRECTIVE

DATA SYSTEM STATUS

ENVIRONMENTAL SENSOR

IG-88

Rogue assassin droid IG-88 has eyes in the back of his head. Rear and front optical sensors allow him to see in every direction at once, so he can be aware of any danger. When he is hired by Darth Vader to capture Han Solo, IG-88 also makes use of other sensors, which allow him to sense movement, register temperature, and see through metal. He uses his multi-faceted vision and his databanks to identify rival bounty hunters and potential targets.

DIRECTIVE PARAMETERS

WEAPON DETECTION

VOICE STRESS ANALYSIS

BATTLE DROID

Battle droids' visual sensors are no sharper than the eyes of an average living being, but the droids' programming allows them to distinguish between friends and foes, and seek out targets and objectives, as identified by their Droid Control Ship. Such abilities are useful during a furious and fast-paced battle, when droids need to make split-second decisions.

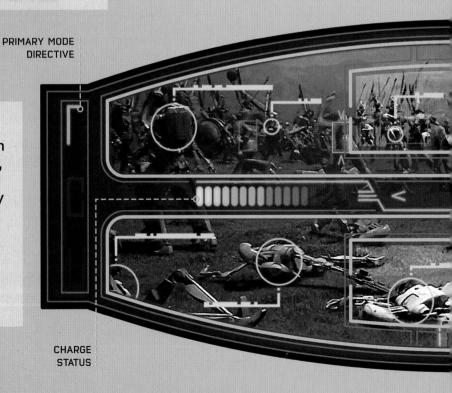

PRIMARY MODE DIRECTIVE

CHARGE STATUS

FOCUSED LIFE-FORM SCAN

THERMOGRAPHIC
PERIMETER SWEEP

SUBJECT
VITAL SIGNS

DROID VISION: COMBAT

OPPOSITION
IDENTIFIER

COMMAND
SIGNAL

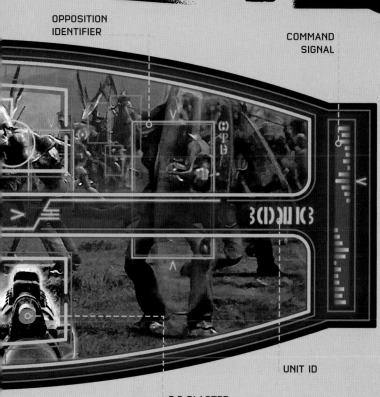

Combat droids are
fitted with multiple
visual sensors and
data displays.
They need to keep
track of many things
at once, including
targets and threats.

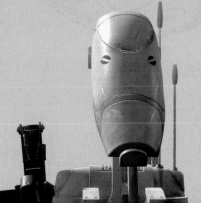

E-5 BLASTER

UNIT ID

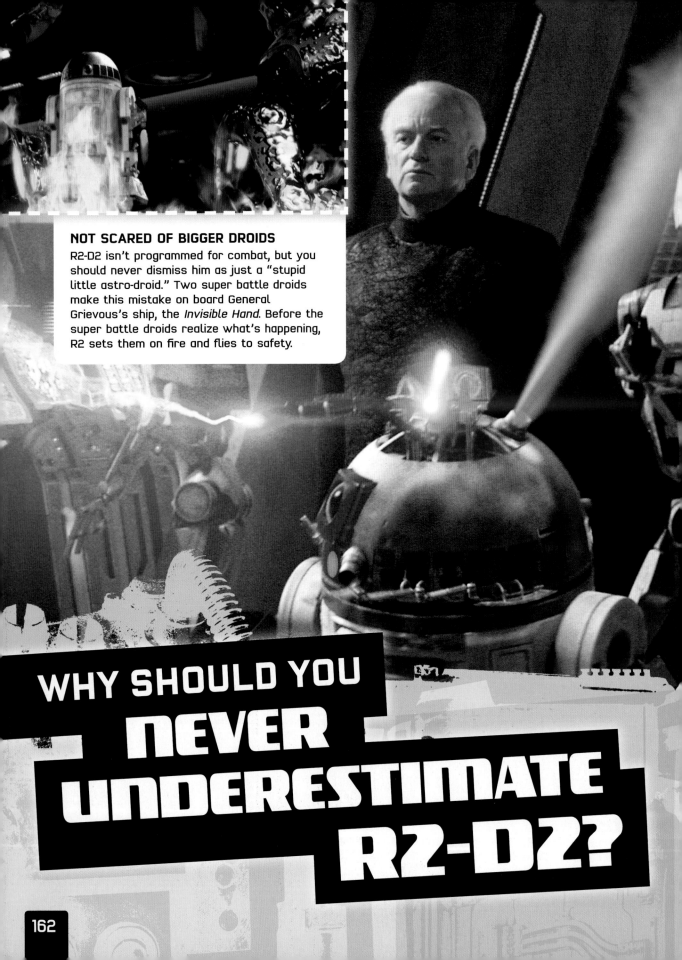

NOT SCARED OF BIGGER DROIDS

R2-D2 isn't programmed for combat, but you should never dismiss him as just a "stupid little astro-droid." Two super battle droids make this mistake on board General Grievous's ship, the *Invisible Hand*. Before the super battle droids realize what's happening, R2 sets them on fire and flies to safety.

WHY SHOULD YOU NEVER UNDERESTIMATE R2-D2?

DISTRACTING DROID

Obi-Wan Kenobi and Anakin Skywalker are captured on Grievous's ship. Suddenly, R2-D2 activates many of his systems, creating a noisy spectacle. While the battle droids are distracted, Obi-Wan and Anakin swing into action and grab their lightsabers!

SMOKESCREEN

R2 and his friends are being chased by stormtroopers on Cloud City! R2-D2 activates his fire extinguisher, filling the air with a cloud of super-cold vapor. The stormtroopers can't see through the murky fire-suppression gas, giving the Rebels time to reach the safety of Han Solo's starship, the *Millennium Falcon*.

R2-D2'S BARREL-SHAPED body contains many tools for repairing starships and helping pilots and mechanics—but the feisty little astromech is rather creative in finding other uses for his tools. When he finds himself in danger, R2 can always come up with a way to defeat or distract the enemies who are threatening him or his friends.

DROID ATTACK!

BATTLE DROIDS
VS
LIGHTSABER

A Jedi like Obi-Wan Kenobi can use his lightsaber to slice right through battle droids' flimsy bodies or to deflect their blaster fire right back at them!

PROBE DROID
VS
BLASTER

Probe droids are big, sneaky, and scary, but with a well-aimed blaster shot, Han Solo causes the probot enough concern that it self-destructs!

CRAB DROID
VS
BLASTER RIFLE

Separatist crab droids are fast, tough, and deadly, but the Republic's clone troopers know how to locate a droid's weak points—like the top of its head!

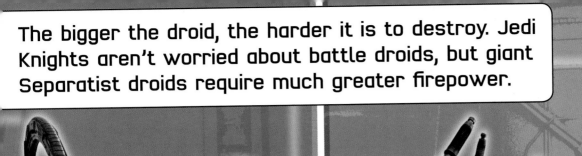

The bigger the droid, the harder it is to destroy. Jedi Knights aren't worried about battle droids, but giant Separatist droids require much greater firepower.

HAILFIRE DROID
VS
REPUBLIC ATTACK GUNSHIP

HOMING SPIDER DROID
VS
AT-TE

Hailfire droids are deadly mobile tanks that demolish enemy troops with their powerful missiles. These speedy Separatist units are best defeated from the air, so the Republic army attacks with laser cannons from their gunships.

Homing spider droids can blast rows of clone troopers or raise their guns to fire at gunships overhead. The Republic strikes back with squads of tough, heavily armed AT-TEs, which take aim at a spider droid's legs or laser dish to destroy it.

HOW DOES C-3PO RELAX?

DROIDS DON'T GET tired like living beings do—but they still need to recharge and repair. C-3PO is programmed to interact with humans, so he sometimes behaves as if he is a tired life-form who needs to take a break from the worry and stress of his daily existence.

PLAYING IT SAFE

Some droids relax by playing and watching games, but C-3PO is more interested in safety as he watches Chewbacca and R2-D2 play a game of Dejarik aboard the *Millennium Falcon*. When Chewbacca becomes angry at R2-D2, Han Solo warns C-3PO that Wookiees sometimes tear their opponents' arms off when they lose. Now all C-3PO can think about is making sure R2 lets the Wookiee win!

QUIET TIME

After C-3PO loses an arm in a fall on Tatooine, Luke Skywalker repairs the golden droid. C-3PO shuts down for a little while so his damaged systems will repair more quickly.

A LONG SOAK

After Owen Lars buys him from Jawa traders, C-3PO isn't very happy to be stuck on a moisture farm. But at least he has time to take a soothing oil bath. His joints are full of Tatooine's sand and grit!

KIND MASTER

Luke Skywalker lowers his uncle's new protocol droid, C-3PO, into an oil bath. He knows that a happy droid is a helpful droid.

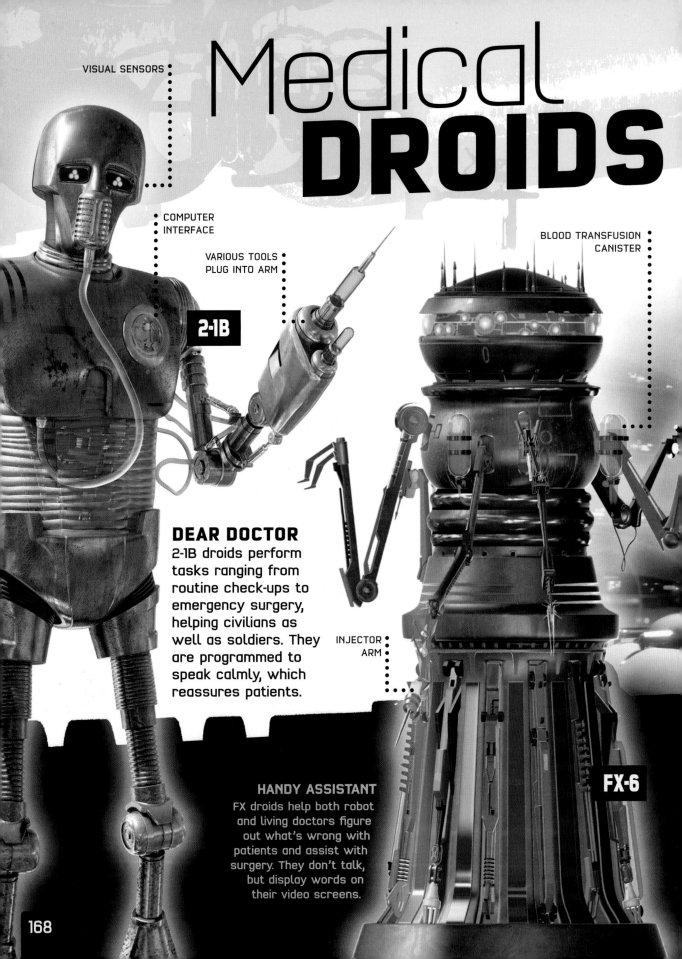

VISUAL SENSORS

Medical
DROIDS

COMPUTER INTERFACE

VARIOUS TOOLS PLUG INTO ARM

2-1B

BLOOD TRANSFUSION CANISTER

DEAR DOCTOR
2-1B droids perform tasks ranging from routine check-ups to emergency surgery, helping civilians as well as soldiers. They are programmed to speak calmly, which reassures patients.

INJECTOR ARM

FX-6

HANDY ASSISTANT
FX droids help both robot and living doctors figure out what's wrong with patients and assist with surgery. They don't talk, but display words on their video screens.

CARING

On Polis Massa, a gentle midwife droid helps Padmé Amidala through the birth of her and Anakin's twins, Luke and Leia. The midwife droid ensures that the babies are healthy and safe, even though she cannot save Padmé.

ECHO BASE DOCTOR

After Luke Skywalker nearly dies in a blizzard on Hoth, a 2-1B droid supervises his treatment. He places Luke in a healing bacta tank until he is sure that the Jedi is fully recovered.

MIDWIFE DROID

Medical droids are robot doctors, whose memory banks are crammed full of information about diseases and injuries. They know how to treat thousands of different species. Galactic citizens rely on medical droids for both routine and emergency care.

MEDICAL DROID

MANUFACTURER: VARIOUS
HEIGHT: VARIES
GENDER: VARIES
FEATURES: MEDICAL TOOLS, INTEGRATED DISEASE DATABASE, NUTRIENT FLUIDS, PROGRAMMED FOR PRECISION, SOOTHING VOICE (MIDWIFE DROIDS)

DROIDS GONE WRONG

Droids are supposed to obey their programming, but software errors or bad wiring can cause malfunctions that turn droids into liars, thieves, or worse. Unscrupulous owners have also been known to reprogram their droids to do harm to others. Such renegade droids are rare, but living beings greatly fear them.

GAS CANISTERS

IG-88

MODIFIED E-11 BLASTER

DAMAGE-RESISTANT SERVO WIRING

ROGUE ROBOT

The IG-series of assassin droids was produced by Holowan Mechanicals, which also created MagnaGuards. When activated, the first IG-88 unit destroyed its creators because it viewed them as a threat. IG-88 became a rogue droid, operating under his own orders in search of profit.

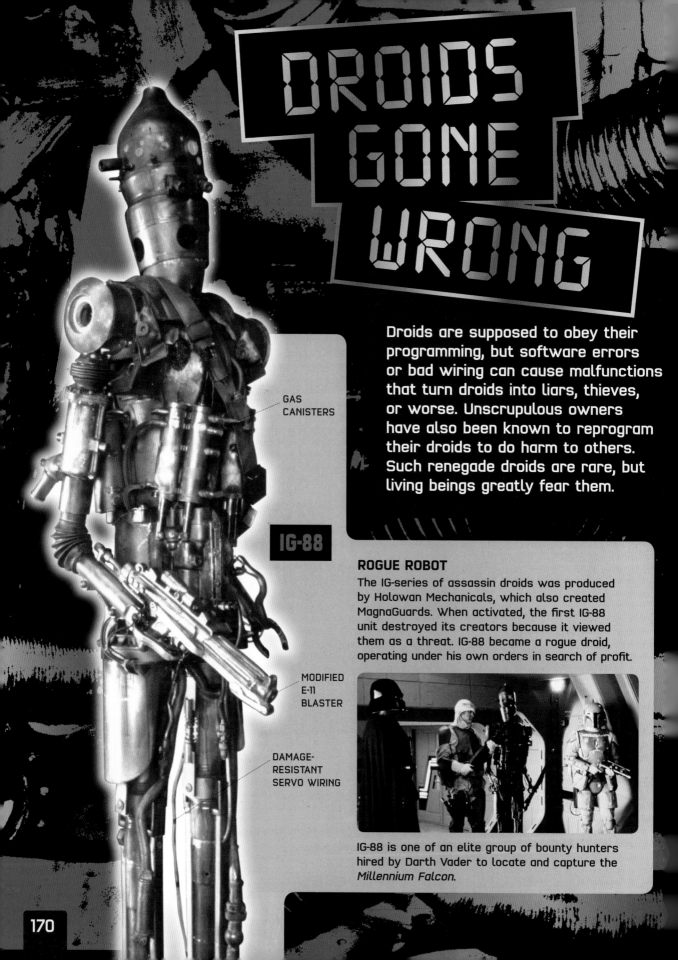

IG-88 is one of an elite group of bounty hunters hired by Darth Vader to locate and capture the *Millennium Falcon*.

INSECTILE HEAD

DANGEROUS DROID

4-LOM is a protocol droid who originally worked as a valet on a luxury spaceliner. The crafty droid overwrote his own programming and became a jewel thief. As a rogue droid, 4-LOM was free to pursue his own evil agenda, eventually becoming a deadly bounty hunter.

RUSTY DROID PLATING

4-LOM

8D8

CAPTIVE POWER DROID

METAL MONSTER

8D8 droids work in metal-smelting plants where it's too hot for living beings. An 8D8 droid was purchased by Jabba the Hutt and reprogrammed to torment other droids in Jabba's palace. He works together with EV-9D9.

LEVER FOR PORTABLE SMELTER

SADISTIC SUPERVISOR

MerenData accidentally built its EV supervisor droids with parts from interrogation droids. This made the EV-series malfunction and act cruelly to those under their supervision. EV-9D9 escaped capture and was soon employed by Jabba the Hutt to oversee the droids in his palace. Beware!

DROID COMMAND CONSOLE

EV-9D9

SPINDLY LIMBS

ARE DROIDS ALWAYS RESPECTED?

SOME PEOPLE ARE kind to droids, but many are not. These people do what they like with droids without caring about them. The galaxy is a scary place for droids. Everywhere you look, someone is ready to sell you, trade you, or—worst of all—melt you down!

DON'T SPILL!
R2-D2 is a sophisticated droid built to repair starships and talk to computers, but Jabba the Hutt makes him wear a tray and serve drinks. R2, however, doesn't mind: he knows that this is all part of a plan to rescue Han Solo. The little droid has Luke Skywalker's lightsaber concealed inside his dome!

DIRTY WORK

C-3PO speaks millions of languages and can help diplomats during important meetings. But after Luke gives him to Jabba as a gift, C-3PO is forced to translate rude threats made by bounty hunters. And when Jabba doesn't like what he hears, he takes his anger out on his "talk droid." C-3PO often finds himself covered in green slime from Jabba's dinner!

GATHERING DUST

Captured by Jawas, C-3PO and R2-D2 find themselves surrounded by battered, broken droids inside a sandcrawler. The Jawas plan to sell these droids, but in the meantime, they are piled up and left to rust—as if they were scrap metal. C-3PO and R2 hope they don't end up like that!

After Count Dooku cut off Anakin's arm, Anakin replaced the lost limb with a mechanical one, hidden by a black glove.

DROID

Anakin's right hand and part of his forearm are mechanical.
TOTAL: 10%

NOT DROID

The rest of Anakin is flesh and blood— at least until his duel with Obi-Wan Kenobi.
TOTAL: 90%

WAT TAMBOR

A member of the Separatist Council, Wat Tambor wears an environment suit that mimics the high pressure of his home planet, Skako.

DROID

Tambor looks like a droid, but he is actually a living being in protective gear.
TOTAL: 0%

NOT DROID

Skakoans like Wat are used to higher pressure and an atmosphere rich in methane.
TOTAL: 100%

DROID OR NOT?

LOBOT

Lobot is chief aide to Cloud City's Baron Lando Calrissian. His brain is connected directly to his city's central computer.

DROID

Lobot's implant attaches to his brain, allowing him to talk to Cloud City's computers just by thinking.
TOTAL: 10%

NOT DROID

Lobot is a living being, but he prefers to communicate using his thoughts instead of actually speaking.
TOTAL: 90%

After nearly being killed in a duel with Obi-Wan Kenobi, Vader is fitted with artificial limbs and life-supporting armor. He cannot survive without them.

DROID
Vader's arms and legs are mechanical, as are some of his organs. Machines help him breathe, see, hear, and speak.
TOTAL: 80%

NOT DROID
Vader may have forgotten the feel of rain or fresh air, but beneath his armor some of his humanity still remains.
TOTAL: 20%

DARTH VADER

DROID
Grievous's limbs, body, and even parts of his head are artificial.
TOTAL: 95%

Grievous was once a Kaleesh warlord, but since being injured in an explosion, most of his body has been replaced by armored parts.

NOT DROID
Grievous's eyes, brain, spinal cord, and organs are organic. Be warned, he hates being called a droid!
TOTAL: 5%

Some beings look like droids, but they are really cyborgs; living beings with mechanical parts. Sometimes, these parts replace lost limbs or organs, and sometimes they make a life-form stronger or faster. But remember: just because a cyborg is part-robot, it doesn't make him a droid!

GENERAL GRIEVOUS

The B'omarr monks live in Jabba the Hutt's palace. They have thrown away their bodies so their brains can live forever in jars.

DROID
The monks' brain-jars are carried in modified droids that look like huge spiders.
TOTAL: 99%

NOT DROID
The brain floating in its nutrient fluid is all that remains of the monk's body.
TOTAL: 1%

B'omarr monk

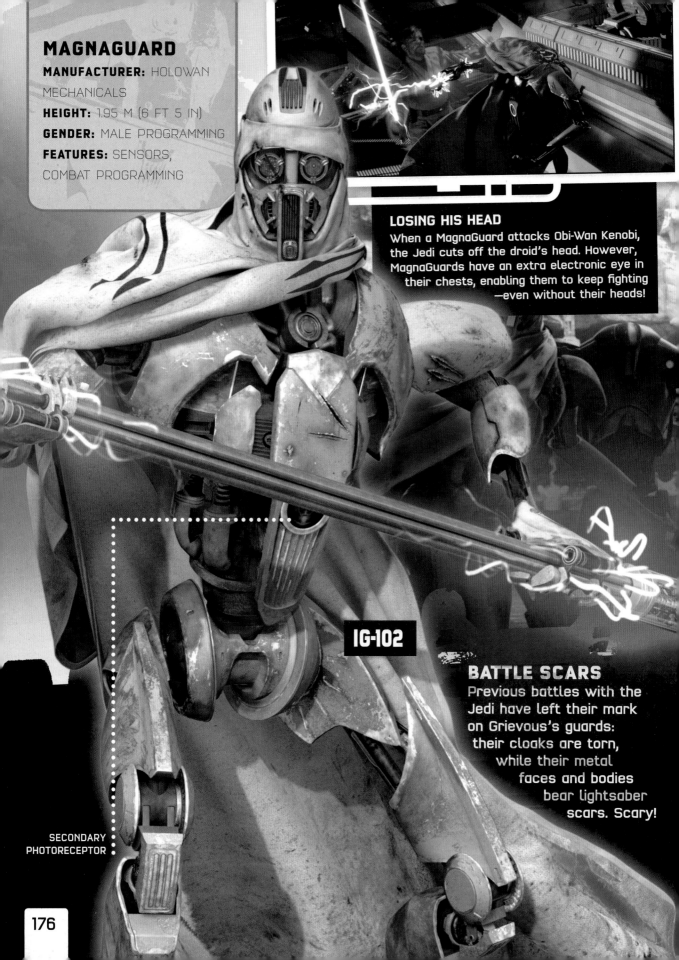

MAGNAGUARD

MANUFACTURER: HOLOWAN MECHANICALS
HEIGHT: 1.95 M (6 FT 5 IN)
GENDER: MALE PROGRAMMING
FEATURES: SENSORS, COMBAT PROGRAMMING

LOSING HIS HEAD

When a MagnaGuard attacks Obi-Wan Kenobi, the Jedi cuts off the droid's head. However, MagnaGuards have an extra electronic eye in their chests, enabling them to keep fighting —even without their heads!

IG-102

BATTLE SCARS

Previous battles with the Jedi have left their mark on Grievous's guards: their cloaks are torn, while their metal faces and bodies bear lightsaber scars. Scary!

SECONDARY PHOTORECEPTOR

DON'T TOUCH!

The glowing tips of MagnaGuards' electrostaffs can stun or kill. Electrostaffs are made of phrik, a tough metal that resists even a lightsaber's cutting power.

DURASTEEL LIMBS

DEADLY ELECTROSTAFF

DARK DEFENDERS

MagnaGuards protect General Grievous on the planet Utapau. Obi-Wan Kenobi must defeat these grim bodyguards before he can duel Grievous himself.

IG-101

MAGNETIC FEET

MAGNAGUARDS

Terrifying MagnaGuards protect the Separatists' most important leaders, such as Count Dooku and General Grievous. Their advanced combat programming makes them very dangerous indeed. MagnaGuards are specially programmed to attack and destroy Jedi Knights.

SERVING THE DARK SIDE

Droids' actions are determined by their programming—they have no choice. Some droids become servants of the dark side because they are designed for evil purposes, or because their masters order them to.

"CHOPPER" DROID

These medical droids got their grim nickname by operating on living beings to give them artificial limbs and organs. Choppers help entomb Darth Vader in his life-preserving armor.

VIPER PROBE DROID

Probe droids have been used by military forces for centuries. The Empire dispatches frightening, black-armored probots to hunt for Luke Skywalker and his Rebel friends.

ASN-121 ASSASSIN DROID

The bounty hunter Zam Wesell sends this flying assassin droid to Padmé Amidala's apartment, where it releases poisonous kouhun insects into her bedroom.

SITH PROBE DROID

Darth Maul sends three "dark eye" probes across Tatooine in search of Padmé Amidala and her Jedi companions. These small droids can search for their targets while hovering above crowds.

IT-O INTERROGATION DROID

These cruel droids are programmed to terrify the Empire's prisoners. They have mechanical arms tipped with frightening tools, which often intimidate the prisoners into revealing their deepest secrets.

RA-7 PROTOCOL DROID

These grim-faced protocol droids are so common aboard the Death Star that they are nicknamed "Death Star droids." They secretly spy on their masters to make sure they stay loyal to the Empire.

IMPERIAL ASTROMECHS

Astromech droids serve the pilots and mechanics of the Empire, too. R2-Q5 and R5-J2 are two of the droids waiting aboard the second Death Star to greet Emperor Palpatine when he visits the station during construction above the green Endor Moon.

DO DROIDS HAVE FRIENDS?

MOST CITIZENS OF THE galaxy rarely wonder what their droids are thinking or feeling. And most droids only do what they're programmed to do; they don't talk to others unless they need to. But sometimes droids do form friendships, either with other droids, or with living beings who don't just treat them like machines.

DROID DATA

■ Most droids receive regular memory wipes, so they often don't remember things they've said or done. Droids are more likely to develop personalities if their masters don't erase their memories.

GETTING ALONG

Chewbacca often gets annoyed because C-3PO complains about everything, while C-3PO thinks Chewie should control his temper better. But Chewie tries to repair C-3PO after stormtroopers blast him on Cloud City. C-3PO gets angry when he realizes his head is on backward, but deep down is grateful for the Wookiee's efforts.

EWOK FRIEND

Feisty little R2-D2 is annoyed when the Ewoks take him and his friends prisoner, and he tries to zap the furry creatures with electric shocks. But after he calms down, R2 finds that he's quite fond of Wicket. The Ewok is small but brave—just like R2.

PARTNERS IN BATTLE

Most starship pilots view their astro-droids as pieces of equipment. But Anakin Skywalker has known R2-D2 for many years, and thinks of him as a trusty friend. Anakin can often understand the little droid's whistles and beeps, which helps them work as team, both in space and on land.

SAVING THE GALAXY

Most droids spend their days doing the dull jobs they are assigned by their owners. But some droids have a higher calling: R2-D2 and C-3PO help their masters save the galaxy from evil!

A CALL FOR HELP
When General Grievous kidnaps Chancellor Palpatine, Anakin Skywalker and Obi-Wan Kenobi race to save the Republic's leader. They are trapped inside an elevator on Grievous's starship, and call R2-D2 for help. Can he get the elevator running again?

CAUGHT IN A TRAP
Luke Skywalker and Han Solo disguise themselves as stormtroopers on their mission to rescue Princess Leia from the Death Star. However, all three of them—and Chewie—end up trapped in a trash masher. Can R2 stop the compactor before the Rebel heroes are crushed?

AVOIDING THE GUARDS
On the moon of Endor, Han, Leia, and Chewbacca lead a mission to destroy the energy shield that protects the second Death Star. They must break into an Imperial bunker, but it is heavily guarded by stormtroopers.

DROID TO THE RESCUE!

R2-D2 knows Obi-Wan and Anakin need him, but he's got bigger problems: two hulking super battle droids are searching for him. R2 defeats the droids easily and then races off to rescue the Jedi. He receives Obi-Wan's instructions via his comlink and takes control of the elevator with his computer interface arm.

QUICK THINKING

While C-3PO urges his friend to hurry, R2-D2 taps into the Death Star's computer network, locates the garbage compactors, and shuts them down. The Rebels are saved with just moments to spare! C-3PO should be relieved when he hears his friends yelling happily, but the anxious droid thinks they are screaming in pain!

INTO THE WOODS

C-3PO and R2-D2 distract as many stormtroopers as they can and lead them on a chase through the woods. Endor's Ewok warriors are ready to ambush the troopers, giving Han and Leia a chance to destroy the energy shield before the Rebel fleet arrives to attack the Death Star.

GLOSSARY

ASTROMECH DROID
■ A utility robot that repairs and helps navigate starships.

BACTA
■ A healing chemical substance used in hospitals across the galaxy.

BATTLE DROID
■ A Separatist robot designed for combat.

BATTLE OF CORUSCANT
■ Clone Wars conflict in 19 BBY where the Separatist army attacks the planet Coruscant kidnapping Supreme Chancellor Palpatine.

BATTLE OF ENDOR
■ Conflict in 4 ABY where the Rebel Alliance attacks Imperial forces on the moon of Endor, resulting in the destruction of the second Death Star and marking the decline of the Empire.

BATTLE OF GEONOSIS
■ Conflict in 22 BBY where the Republic's clone army attacks the Separatists' battle droid army on the planet Geonosis, marking the start of the Clone Wars.

BATTLE OF HOTH
■ Conflict in 3 ABY where Imperial forces attack Rebel headquarters Echo Base on the planet Hoth.

BATTLE OF KASHYYYK
■ Conflict in 19 BBY where the Separatists' droid army fights against the Wookiees and Jedi on the planet Kashyyyk.

BATTLE OF NABOO
Conflict in 32 BBY where the Trade Federation invades the planet Naboo with their battle droid army.

BATTLE OF YAVIN
■ Conflict in Year 0 where Rebel forces based on the moon Yavin 4, attack and destroy the first Imperial Death Star.

BLOCKADE
■ A political strategy that prevents food and resources from reaching a specific destination.

BOLA
■ A throwing weapon made up of a rope with stones at each end.

BOUNTY HUNTER
■ Someone who tracks down, captures, or destroys wanted people for a fee.

BUZZ DROIDS
■ Small droids that latch onto and sabotage enemy spacecraft; often used by Separatist forces in space battles.

CHANCELLOR
■ The title given to the head of the Galactic Senate and Republic.

CLONE ARMY
■ An army of genetically identical soldiers, all trained to be perfect warriors. They fight for the Republic.

CLONE WARS
■ A series of galaxy-wide battles fought between the Republic's clone army and the droid army of the Confederacy of Independent Systems, which took place between 22 and 19 BBY.

COLICOID
■ An insectoid species from the planet Colla IV who are hired to create several battlefield droids for the Separatists.

CORUSCANT
■ The capital of the Republic. This planet is home to the Senate building, the Jedi Temple, and the Jedi Council.

CYBORG
■ A being that is partly a living organism and partly a robot.

DARK SIDE
■ The evil side of the Force that feeds off negative emotions and offers raw power to those who study it.

DEATH STAR
■ A planet-sized battle station built by the Empire which has enough firepower to destroy an entire planet.

DEMOCRACY
■ A system of government where all senior politicians are elected by the population.

DIPLOMAT
■ A person who conducts negotiations and builds relationships with people from other planets and cultures.

DROIDEKA
■ A destroyer droid used in battle by the Separatists.

DRONE
■ A worker who obeys the orders of others and has no authority of his own.

ECHO BASE
■ The headquarters of the Rebel Alliance, located on the ice planet Hoth.

ELECTROSTAFF
Weapon favored by General Grievous and his MagnaGuard bodyguards.

EMPEROR
■ Ruler of the Empire.

EMPIRE
■ A tyrannical power that rules the galaxy from 19BBY to 4 ABY under the leadership of the Emperor, who is a Sith Lord.

FAMBAA

 Four-legged creature used by the Gungan Army to support their shield generators.

FORCE

■ The energy that flows through all living things, which can be used for either good or evil.

FORCE LIGHTNING

■ Deadly rays of blue energy that can be used as a weapon by someone who has embraced the dark side of the Force.

GALACTIC CIVIL WAR

■ Conflict between 2 BBY and 4 ABY in which the Rebel Alliance opposes and fights against the Galactic Empire.

GEONOSIS

■ A rocky, desert planet on the Outer Rim Territories, famous for its droid factories.

GRAND MASTER

■ The leader of the Jedi Council.

GUNGANS

■ An amphibious species from the planet Naboo.

GYROSCOPE

■ A spinning device that helps objects maintain their balance.

HOTH

■ An ice-covered planet located in the remote sector o the Outer Rim Territories.

HYPERSPACE

■ An extra dimension of space, used by experienced starship pilots to travel fast that the speed of light using a hyperdrive.

JAWAS

■ A species of small creatures native to the planet Tatooine. They trade scrap metal found in the desert.

JEDI

■ An ancient sect of Force-sensitives who study the light side and the use of their powers for the good of the galaxy.

JEDI COUNCIL

■ The 12 senior, respected members of the Jedi Order who meet to make important decisions and give advice.

JEDI KNIGHT

■ A member of the Jedi Order who has studied as a Padawan under a Jedi Master and has passed the Jedi Trials.

JEDI MASTER

■ A rank for Jedi Knights who have performed an exceptional deed or have trained a Jedi Knight.

JEDI ORDER

■ An ancient organization that promotes peace and justice throughout the galaxy.

JEDI PURGE

■ The attempt by Chancellor Palpatine in 19 BBY to annihilate the entire Jedi Order.

JEDI TEMPLE

■ The headquarters of the Jedi Order, located on the planet Coruscant.

KAADU

■ Loyal, gentle creatures native to Naboo. Gungan soldiers use them as mount in battle.

KAMA

■ A protective addition to clone trooper armor, worn around the waist.

KAMINO

■ A stormy, ocean planet on which the clone army was built, located beyond the Outer Rim.

KASHYYYK

■ A jungle planet where the Wookiees live, located in the Mid Rim.

LIGHTSABER

■ A weapon with a blade of pure energy that is used by Jedi and Sith warriors.

NABOO

■ A beautiful planet near the border of the Outer Rim Territories.

ORDER 66

■ An order given by Chancellor Palpatine that begins the Jedi Purge. Every trooper in the clone army is ordered to kill all the Jedi.

PADAWAN

■ A Youngling who is chosen to serve an apprenticeship with a Jedi Master.

PODRACING

■ A popular sport in which competitors race against each other in high-powered vehicles

PROBE DROID

■ Imperial robot that gathers and transmits data.

REBEL ALLIANCE

■ The organization that resists and fights against the Empire.

REPUBLIC

■ The long-standing government of the galaxy, under leadership of an elected Chancellor.

SANDCRAWLER

■ A large transport vehicle that travels well over sand, often used by Jawa tribes as mobile bases.

SENATE

■ Government of the Republic, with representatives from all parts of the galaxy.

SENATOR

■ A person who represents their planet, sector, or system in the Senate.

SEPARATISTS

■ An alliance against the Republic. Also known as the Confederacy of Independent System.

SITH

■ An ancient sect of Force-sensitives who study the dark side to gain control and succeed in their greedy plans.

TATOOINE

■ A desert planet with two suns located in the Outer Rim Territories. Known as a meeting place for criminals and smugglers.

TRADE FEDERATION

■ A bureaucratic organization that controls much of the trade and commerce in the galaxy.

YOUNGLING

■ A Force-sensitive child who joins the Jedi Order to be trained in the Jedi arts.

INDEX

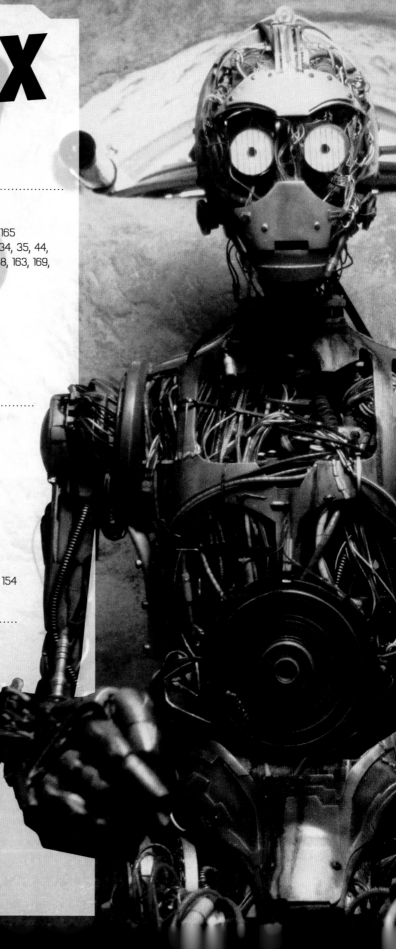

LONDON, NEW YORK, MELBOURNE,
MUNICH, AND DELHI

For Dorling Kindersley
Editors Tori Kosara, Shari Last,
Julia March, Helen Murray
Designers Clive Savage, Lisa Sodeau,
Rhys Thomas, Toby Truphet
Design Manager Maxine Pedliham
Managing Editor Laura Gilbert
Art Director Lisa Lanzarini
Publishing Director Simon Beecroft
Publishing Manager Julie Ferris

Project Manager Sarah Harland
DTP Designer Kavita Varma
Editorial Assistant Lauren Nesworthy
Senior Producer Verity Powell

For Lucasfilm
Executive Editor J. W. Rinzler
Art Director Troy Alders
Keeper of the Holocron Leland Chee
Director of Publishing Carol Roeder

This edition published in 2014
First published in the United States in 2012 by DK Publishing
345 Hudson Street, New York, New York 10014

001–270706–Sep/2014

First published as two separate titles: Star Wars®: *The Secret Life
of Droids* (2011), Star Wars®: *Battles for the Galaxy* (2011)

A catalog record for this book is available
from the Library of Congress.

ISBN: 978-1-4654-2635-2

Color reproduction by Media Development Printing Ltd, UK
Printed and bound by Leo Paper Products, China

The publisher would like to thank Chris Reiff and Chris Trevas
for their artwork on pages 66–69 and Jo Casey for her editorial
assistance. Lucasfilm would like to thank Jann Moorhead and
David Anderman.

Discover more at
www.dk.com
www.starwars.com